1973

Caring for Your Aging Parents

Caring for Your Aging Parents

*A Concerned, Complete Guide
for Children of the Elderly*

Robert R. Cadmus, M.D., D.Sc.

Prentice-Hall, Inc.

Englewood Cliffs, New Jersey

Prentice-Hall International, Inc., *London*
Prentice-Hall of Australia, Pty. Ltd., *Sydney*
Prentice-Hall Canada, Inc., *Toronto*
Prentice-Hall of India Private Ltd., *New Delhi*
Prentice-Hall of Japan, Inc., *Tokyo*
Prentice-Hall of Southeast Asia Pte., Ltd., *Singapore*
Whitehall Books, Ltd., *Wellington, New Zealand*
Editora Prentice-Hall do Brasil, Ltda., *Rio de Janeiro*

© 1984 by

Prentice-Hall, Inc.
Englewood Cliffs, New Jersey

Library of Congress Cataloging in Publication Data

Cadmus, Robert R.
  Caring for your aging parents.

  Includes index.
  1. Parents, Aged--United States--Family relationships.
  2. Parents, Aged--United States--Care and hygiene.
  3. Retirement--United States. 4. Adult children--United
States--Family relationships. I. Title.
HQ1064.U5C33 1984   646.7'8   84-3356

ISBN 0-13-114786-2
ISBN 0-13-114752-8 {PBK}

Printed in the United States of America

Foreword

Every trend in society points to the timeliness of this exceptional book—our aging population, the increasing dispersion of the tightly knit family, the evolving economic and political environment, the high cost of medical care, the changing roles of agencies and institutions, and even our own attitudes toward both aging and the aged.

The text is a thoughtful mixture of inspiration, hard facts, and helpful hints, which should significantly benefit both the reader and his or her aging parents. Obviously the author gives no simple solution to the handling of one's parents. There is none. No two elderly persons are alike. However, Dr. Cadmus has distilled and accumulated in one volume the current state of the art in dealing with a myriad of problems affecting the elderly and those who are close to them. The wealth of his personal and professional experience gives this book an authenticity and relevance not usually seen in texts on this subject.

The purpose of the book is not to amuse but to educate, although the author does it in a uniquely readable and understandable style. He builds upon the simple fact that the skill in handling and caring for one's aging parents is not instinctive. Rather, there are facts to learn, behavior to understand, attitudes to develop, and practices to perfect. Furthermore, parents and their children alter their relationship throughout their lives. Consequently another role change may be necessary when parents age.

If you have parents or even aging friends or relatives, this book is a necessity. Certainly the elderly segment of our society will be better off because of what this book teaches, and you in turn will save yourself the pain of unfounded guilt or regrets because of the way you may be tempted to act. What's more, the same knowledge will help you age

more gracefully and will teach you what to expect when it's your turn
to become an aging parent.

SIDNEY SHINDELL, M.D., LL.B.
Chairman and Professor
Department of Preventive Medicine
Medical College of Wisconsin
November 1983

Acknowledgments

I wish to express my deep appreciation to my wife, Lorna, whose encouragement, advice, and skillful proofreading helped me prepare the manuscript; to my students in Preventive Medicine whose reports on the families they studied convinced me that there was a need for this book; to Virginia Kraucunas, the *Milwaukee Journal*, and the *Milwaukee Sentinel* for their touching photographs; and to all my contemporaries about whom I have written with affection.

Contents

CHAPTER 1

It's
Your
Problem

Photo courtesy of Milwaukee Journal

*D*o you take care of your aging parents as well as you should? I doubt it. Few of us do. It is a subject we tend to ignore until it is too late, then we feel guilty about it for the rest of our days, wishing we had acted differently. But for you it is not too late. You can still learn how to take care of your aging parents and do it with complete satisfaction both to yourself and to them.

As you might expect, I include in the term *parents* not only all biological parents but also all maligned mothers-in-law, all forgotten fathers-in-law, stepmothers and stepfathers, and adoptive and foster parents as well.

Incidentally, it would be helpful if the same thoughtful care could be showered upon your elderly aunts and uncles, and even better if it could be extended to your elderly neighbors. This is particularly important because there is a temporary increase in the number of orphaned elderly—those without children—due to the low birth rates during the post-Depression years of the early thirties. Unless some of their care can be assumed by loving relatives or friends or by some charitable organization, their golden years will be considerably tarnished. Although our government will supply them with a "safety net," that will include little more than the bare necessities of life.

For the majority of American families, the lives of three generations overlap one another: grandparents, parents, and children. If these three generations are related by blood, marriage, or adoption and live either in the same house or close enough for frequent communication, they are considered to be an extended family. Chances are your parents grew up in such a household. Although many social scientists recommend such living arrangements, today only 70 percent of white families and 56 percent of nonwhite families are lucky enough to be even considered a nuclear family—one with a husband, wife, and nonadult children. The remainder live in one-parent families headed primarily by women, an increasing number of whom are under thirty-five years of age.

However, as life expectancy increases, the numbers of families enjoying four or more generations will also increase. That will further extend, if not overburden, the few remaining extended families. But the immediate impact of this growing longevity is that more and more middle-aged people will have living parents. In fact, one-third of those who are now sixty years old still have at least one living parent.

3

Therefore, caring for one's aging parents is not a problem confined to a few middle years. It may extend over decades. In fact, that happened in my own family. My wife and I were sixty-four before we lost the last of our parents.

If either the good Lord or the mortality statistics, whichever you would prefer to credit, have been kind enough to permit your parents to survive into old age, the information contained in these pages might be put to use four times during your lifetime. On the other hand, some of it might not. Some middle-aged sons and daughters experience essentially no problems with their aging parents, some only for the last few weeks or months, some only off and on, and others for years on end. Unfortunately, at your stage of the game you have no way of knowing what the future will hold. What is more, you could not materially change it if you tried. Your only recourse is to be prepared and forewarned that whatever happens will in some way or another also involve you and your entire family. So plan to take it a day at a time and see what happens.

Do not think that the graying of America will be static; that each generation of oldsters will mimic the one that preceded it. Quite to the contrary, as each generation moves from middle age to old age, it carries forward its own sets of values, its own unique heritage, its own individuality. Those who are turning sixty-five today are different from their forefathers. In fact, the final report of the 1981 White House Conference on Aging characterized the nation's elderly as the "wealthiest, best fed, best housed, healthiest, most self-reliant older population in our history." The report could have added that they are also the best educated and have influenced the decisions of society more than any previous generation. Consequently, do not expect the senior citizens of today to accept a downtrodden old age. They will continue their activism and will flaunt their political power. Actually, the same White House Conference has already given them their agenda: strengthening of the Social Security system, more in-home and community services, a more responsive health care system, and the prohibition of mandatory retirement at any age.

I expect the elderly to show the same spirit when it comes to family affairs. They will not be cast aside. They will continue to control their own lives, to make their own choices, and do their own thing. Yet they will exhibit many annoying inconsistencies. They will create ambivalent feelings in you that are difficult to fathom and particularly difficult to handle. At times they will continue to act as your parents. They will dominate you. They will influence your decisions, and they will try to control your life as long as they can get away with it. They will closely watch the unfolding of the fantasies that they held concerning you and your career, and they will wish for you an independence that they may never have tasted. Yet at other times they will show a childlike dependence. They will seek your help, your support, and even your reassurance in regard to the decisions they make. They will expect you to assume any necessary sacrifice, except probably financial, to care for them in their old age on the understandable theory that because they brought you into this world, you owe them that in return. At times they will go out gallivanting when you think they should be home resting, and at other times they will stay home when you think they should be out exercising. They will certainly not follow the patterns your grandparents set. They will be different, and you will have to adjust your care to meet their new standards.

As I look back at what was happening in this country some two decades ago—civil rights demonstrations, the Vietnam War, the drug scene, and the antiestablishment counterculture—and think of the many students I worked with as the president of a medical and dental college during those volatile years, I would wager that many of you and your parents were, to put it mildly, not on the best of terms. Your mores and those of your parents clashed, some more than others. As a result, there were conflicts; words were spoken; threats were made; and doors were slammed. They were not the best of times for either you or your parents.

For the most part those dark days are over. You have put on another twenty years and probably another twenty pounds, and your previously distraught mothers and fathers have now become your aging parents. They may or may not have mellowed over the long years, and they may or may not have forgiven you the events of your past. However, you should have matured and gained in stature and wisdom. Therefore, you now have the golden opportunity to assume the role of peacemaker, to help melt away any guilt or misgivings either you or your parents may have accumulated over the years. By so doing, you will be a better middle-aged son or daughter, and your parents will be better off for it. Fortunately, most feuding families have reunited, reconciled their differences, and discovered that in order to survive in the 1980s people need each other more than at any other time in recent memory. Believe me, you and your aging parents are no exceptions.

You may not remember the problems your parents had in caring for your grandparents. You may not have been home enough to observe how your parents handled them. Therefore, the problems of caring for your own folks may be new to you, even frightening. As I have warned, times have changed and expectations have increased. It is a whole new ball game. You will have to learn the new rules.

Unfortunately, the burden of caring for aging parents can come at a very awkward time. You may be struggling to bring up your own children or trying to understand their rather bizarre lifestyles. You may be struggling to pay for their college education at a time when orthodontia and a dozen other demands have already drained your limited resources. If you are a woman, you may be going through menopause, which is not the ideal time to take on any new problems. If you are a man, you may be seeing your career peak long before you have had time to plan for your retirement. You may have already become an aging parent in your own right, hoping only to find peace and comfort in your remaining years. Then, at some unexpected moment, the problems of your aging parents come tumbling down on you like a ton of bricks. At times it is almost too much to bear.

In fact, for some it is indeed too much. Researchers at the Brookdale Center on Aging at Hunter College have studied the sacrifices that many have been forced to make, and their conclusions are not reassuring. Apparently, one-third of the adults involved in caring for elderly parents report that they suffered some deterioration of their own health; almost one-half developed mental tension in the form of anxiety or depression; one-fourth performed less effectively on their jobs; and another one-fourth worsened their own financial situation. These are high prices to pay. Even your parents will agree to that. Therefore, one must ask, "Can the same care be given without these heavy costs?" Yes, I think it can. At least, the burden can be considerably lightened. Fortunately, like most skills, the art of caring for your aging parents can be learned. Although some of this involves specific do's and don'ts, much of it is more subtle and personal. For you to become an effective participant in your parents' care, you will have to understand the types of problems you will face, become familiar with the various needs of old people, recognize the value of adequate planning, and sense the necessity for greater cooperation between all facets of society. But above all, it will require you to develop a loving and sympathetic attitude—and a real commitment.

You are not the only one who has to show love and commitment or make a sacrifice. Your parents must understand certain hard facts: the time you have to give, your financial resources, the needs of your children, their own degree of preparation for old age, and the limitations of government and social agencies.

At times you will also be required to accept the bitter fact that some problems have no solution and that personal satisfaction must come from trying, not from getting results. Many middle-aged people fail to distinguish between trying and unsatisfactory results. Consequently, they try to move the immovable and then feel guilty for their lack of success. In those cases, there should be no guilt. Unfortunately, all loving, wonderful people do not grow old gracefully, regardless of how well they are cared for. To see one of your parents deteriorate either physically or mentally before your very eyes will break your heart, but it should not break your spirit. Should this happen to you, try to accept it and endure it to the best of your ability. Regret it, certainly, but don't harbor guilt.

Although a great deal of research is being conducted on all phases of aging, and many hopeful predictions concerning longevity and disease control are coming out of scientific laboratories throughout this country and abroad, you and your parents must live in the world as you find it today. If and when many of these new and promising medical developments do materialize, they will probably come too late to be of much value to your parents, particularly if they are terminally ill. But remember, they have already benefited from many of yesterday's miracles which are in common use today. That is the way progress works!

Not all of the advances in aging are medical or health related. Many stem from recent social and economic legislation, while others spring from private enterprise. They concern employment, retirement, taxes, payment for medical care, various discounts, senior citizen centers, and support services of all kinds. Fortunately, these are not dreams of tomorrow—they are available today. However, they offer no panacea. If your aging parents have done even a smidgen of planning before old age caught up with them, these developments should help ease their burdens. In turn, they also should assist you in meeting your responsibilities without totally sacrificing your own independence. Take advantage of them whenever and wherever you can.

The purpose of this book is not to burden you with new tasks and responsibilities. Rather, it is to help you lighten those that you either already have or will soon face. Therefore, I will try to provide you with the information you will need in caring for your parents. I will also try to help you resolve the many conflicting demands thrust upon you and to help make the whole process more manageable.

If you are really lucky and do not hide this book as if it came in a plain brown wrapper, it may bring you an unexpected bonus. Your own children may read it some rainy afternoon, so that by the time you begin to slide into your own golden years they will be sufficiently well informed and emotionally capable of being good middle-aged sons and daughters themselves. In turn, if your parents peek at it wondering what you are up to, they will not be offended. They may even learn something new about old age. Being old does not necessarily make one an expert on aging.

And finally, I hope it will help your entire family as you struggle with the age-old problem of trying to enjoy life to the fullest while simultaneously acting like responsible individuals in the care of those who are your elders.

CHAPTER 2

Getting
Old

Somewhere deep within our cellular structure there lies a mysterious time clock that makes us grow old. Although it works differently in each of us, none of us can escape its inevitable toll. Along the way lurk many dangers: accidents, disease, malnutrition, war, even an unhealthy lifestyle. These can, and too often do, cut short an individual's life well before his or her own inner clock runs down.

In spite of all of this mayhem, approximately 5,000 Americans turn sixty-five every day. After subtracting deaths, we still find a net daily increase of some 1,400 individuals over the age of sixty-five. As a result, there are now about 25 million people, almost 12 percent or one in every nine of this country's population, whose inner clocks are still ticking after sixty-five or more years of uninterrupted service. Furthermore, the demographic wizards tell us that by the year 2000, depending, of course, upon the birth and death rates in the meantime, one person in every eight will be past the age of sixty-five. That will amount to approximately 32 million senior citizens, enough to challenge the health planners, enough to excite the medical researchers and drug manufacturers, and hopefully enough to motivate the politicians into solving the long-term problems of Social Security. The social, economic, health, and political implications of this impending increase will be enormous, but I will leave it to the futurists to flesh out the details.

Of real consequence for us today is the fact that the number of old people who have made it past seventy-five is also increasing. This latter group, now called the "old-olds" in contrast to those between sixty-five and seventy-four who are considered the "young-olds," are the ones with the greatest number of problems. They suffer disproportionately from multiple illnesses, loneliness, economic deprivation, and the other ravages of old age.

Nevertheless, our elderly are far from a monolithic group. Some are healthy, others are sick; some are economically well off, others are poor; some are strong-willed, others are weak; some discriminate, others are discriminated against; some are a pleasure to be with, and others are a pain in the neck. But regardless of their health, economic status, race, or personality, they all share certain characteristics. They all fear isolation and loneliness, and, in turn, they all crave love, attention, and personal consideration.

Recently I read of a 78-year-old woman who had been robbed ten times and sexually assaulted once in the home in which she had lived for over fifty years. She sadly confessed, "No one has come to see me in more years than I can remember, except the wrong kind. I don't get a card for my birthday or for Christmas. I haven't had a Christmas present in years."

This is a classic example of isolation. There is not an old person in the world who does not detest isolation and who would not be harmed by it should it occur. With increased loneliness, the individual loses his or her self-confidence and self-esteem and begins to have difficulty in establishing new relationships. Eating no longer has any pleasure, so the individual's nutrition deteriorates, which often leads to serious weight loss, iron deficiency anemia, avitaminosis, protein deficiency, and even dehydration. The loss of independence that haunts isolation like a shadow causes anxiety, guilt, anger, fear, and a sense of vulnerability. A deep depression follows, so that even the few remaining good things in life are lost amid a host of negatives, real or imagined. The elderly think of suicide (but generally not by violent means) time and time again. Rather, they contemplate slower, more subtle forms, such as not eating, not taking their medications, or denying themselves the necessities of life. Thoughts of suicide are particularly common in men over eighty. Therefore, you must be on the lookout for signs of depression and suicidal tendencies. Sometimes these signals are very difficult to identify. Depressed old people are often masters at covering up feelings and are experts at playing games to fool not only physicians, but also family and friends. So be observant. Watch their actions, their weight, their dress, their personal behavior, their speech, even the appearance of the house. If these things change, find out why. Avoid the unfortunate situation of your parents thinking that relief can only be found in death. There are far better alternatives.

Depression is the most frequent symptom one sees in the elderly. Yet, as we have discussed, it is not always apparent to the casual observer. Withdrawal, sleep disturbances, agitation, lessened energy or physical activity, disinterest in things that were previously found to be interesting, even headaches, arthritic symptoms, and other physical complaints emerge as signs of depression. Often this condition is masked by a rapid change in personality. The elderly often seek relief in alcohol, in new and unfamiliar lifestyles, in some consuming activity such as a hobby, shopping, jogging, or anything else new or different—including taking a new mate. In effect, they thrash out against their displeasure with life and doggedly strive to regain their lost sense of independence by using every means possible.

Yet depression need not stem from such a dramatic and tragic situation as total isolation. It can occur from the orderly transfer of responsibility. Take, for example, the executive or politician who has enjoyed all of the perquisites of high rank: a well-appointed office, a staff of obedient secretaries and assistants, expensive business lunches, exclusive clubs, first-class transportation, and all the other trappings of success. At best, retirement can be a letdown for such an individual, and unless prepared, he or she will suffer the same depression, not perhaps from isolation, but from a deprivation of a different kind.

Do not think that this phenomenon occurs only at the two extremes of poverty and affluence. It comes in blue collars as well. Being retired and unable to work at a forge or on a construction site is just as devastating to those workers as loss of employment is to anyone else, and just as likely to lead to depression. Women are not immune. In fact, it can strike the working woman as well as the housewife. The only prevention for isolation is to add a meaningful substitute. I will discuss that subject more in Chapter 8, "Keep 'Em Busy."

Alienation is no better than isolation. Another case that comes to mind is that of a lonely old widow who made arrangements for her own funeral, including a list of those who were to be notified and invited to the simple ceremony. The list did not include her own son. As she put it, "Since he didn't visit me when I was alive, I don't want him there when I'm dead." One must wonder how a mother and her son can become so alienated from each other.

It is true that some elderly individuals, even those who are able to maintain themselves, are difficult to be with. Many complain at length about their problems, large and small; some criticize everything you do and everything your children do; others gossip about people you don't know and couldn't care less about knowing; and most repeat, misplace, spill, and forget to zip their zippers. But they are still your parents. Think back! When you were young, you repeated, misplaced, spilled, and forgot to zip your zippers. Your parents were tolerant then and helped you through those trying times. Now it is your turn to be tolerant and help them through their trying times. Do not let any thoughtless act of either omission or commission come between you and your parents. Do not walk away because something is distasteful. Hang in there. In turn, if your parents become aloof, find out why. They may only be exaggerating something that you would let pass unnoticed. Alienation can sneak up on you. Whether you become alienated from them or they become alienated from you, your parents are likely to suffer the most because they are the most vulnerable.

Many adults have trouble understanding and dealing with their own children. As adults we have forgotten how we felt and how we thought as children. It is equally natural that we should have trouble understanding and dealing with our own parents because we have yet to experience how the elderly feel and think. The simple admonition to "honor thy father and thy mother" may point us in the right direction, but unless family members maintain a close relationship and demonstrate a true commitment to one another, conflicts are likely to break out. Whereas alienation is thought of as keeping people physically and mentally apart, conflict is viewed as a more aggressive type of behavior. It is surprising, tragically surprising, how easily conflicts arise between parents and their grown children. They stem from every conceivable cause: failure to remember birthdays and holidays, differing lifestyles, housing, religious disputes, problems with the sharing of resources, disinterest in each other's health or daily problems, and so on. Many of these conflicts can be resolved by simple, direct conversation; by sitting down and talking things over. Yet do not enter into such confrontations as if you were a labor negotiator. Chances are you will not get a just settlement, regardless of the issue. Give in, compromise, and accept anything reasonable that involves no obvious harm. What other alternatives do you have? You can't win. You can't send your parents to their room without supper. However, you can implant ideas that sooner or later may take root and that hopefully may bring some relief to the problem.

Many conflicts that are too deep-seated and too complex for such informal resolution will require professional help. Most communities have some sort of a counseling service, not only for the elderly, but also for the middle-aged sons or daughters of aging parents. Search for such a facility in your community. You may need it sooner than you think.

I will save an expanded discussion of the problems of deteriorating health until Chapter 10, "Hope for Health." But remember, health is an overpowering concern to the elderly. It is also part of growing old.

Unfortunately, problems of isolation, alienation, and conflict are all too frequent. If you have any doubts about that, read "Dear Abby" or some similar column in your local newspaper. It will take you about a week to recognize fully the problems elderly people raise about their own lives and the tribulations of getting old. Living alone is in itself a chore, and it so frequently complicates illness that the International Classification of Diseases developed by the World

Health Organization has a code for "Persons Living Alone," and it is used all too often. The elderly cannot satisfactorily survive in a vacuum. They need a support system, preferably a loving family. If they are the sole survivor, they will need a family substitute: friends, the church, an agency, or a custodial institution. But support includes more than just food and shelter. It must include love, challenge, encouragement, and an acknowledgment of a person's worth—past, present, and future.

Even if there is no isolation, alienation, or conflict, there is still one more sword of Damocles that precariously hangs over the elderly's heads: the fear of dependency. Actress Helen Hayes put it succinctly when she testified before a Senate hearing that, "It is little things like not being able to go to the refrigerator and get a snack that elderly people miss most. . . . It may not be much, until all the small decisions are taken out of your hands and you find that your great age has reduced you to a child." The need to be independent never leaves the elderly. Yet in our desire to be loving and caring, we overcompensate and treat our parents as if they were our children. In the spirit of kindness we take command; we help them dress; we do their errands; we help them cut their meat; and we bring them the things we think they need. Actually, we bring them dependency. It is interesting to note that fewer widows between the ages of sixty-five and seventy-five live with family members than twenty-five years ago. This is not because they were abandoned. It is because they passionately cherish their independence, cherish their right to do what they want, when they want. Consequently, take warning. Care for your aging parents, but do not assume the role of parent. There is a difference.

Most of us have heard of the term *child abuse*. However, the parallel term *elderly abuse* is less well known. It has not yet gained widespread usage, but it is just as real and just as repugnant. As in child abuse, the harm can be something one does as well as something one neglects to do. Furthermore, it can be harmful not only to the body, but devastating to the mind and to the spirit as well. Unfortunately, the victims of elderly abuse are usually in no position to strike back or protect themselves, and so the problem continues and even gets worse. Recently, in a question and answer column of a daily newspaper, I saw a letter complaining that " . . . so many elderly parents are abandoned by the children they cared for while growing up." The column headline, which read, "Daughter Frolics with Friends While Aged Mother Is Unattended," told it all. I have seen it happen too many times. If an outsider or an institution were to harm an elderly person in such a manner, they would be brought to court and summarily punished. However, when the same transgressions occur within the family, they are viewed as private matters to be settled internally. Old age certainly has enough problems and rough terrain to cross without family members adding to the burden.

As one might expect, older people abuse themselves by reading the obituary notices. Funerals of friends and relatives seem to come in bunches, and naturally this gets them to thinking. Memories become more important because memories are real, something to hang on to; they give security and a sense of self-worth. No wonder the elderly count years as carefully as do children—but for different reasons. It is part of getting old.

Although I have perhaps painted the seamy side of old age, not all senior citizens follow such a sad scenario. For those who have planned for their old age and who are lucky enough to enjoy good health, the post-retirement years can be the best of times for both partners. Many pressures are off. Breadwinners no longer have to get up early in the morning or work late shifts at night; they no longer have to commute, worry about performing to their bosses' satisfaction, or work at dangerous jobs. They find that their relationships with their spouses improve now that they have time for each other. Together they do and see things that they never had time to enjoy before. They contribute to society, work with young people, volunteer for community projects. Many keep their stamina and good health for unbelievable periods. Some never retire and continue to be productive well beyond the statistical norm. A few centenarians even blow out candles for the news media. Many live well to the very end. I have seen some of these lucky souls simply close their eyes as if in sleep when their inner clocks finally run down. Nothing could be more peaceful or more reassuring.

Another happy fact is that the bulk of the elderly folks have living sons and daughters or living sons-in-law and daughters-in-law who are able to take care of them in their old age. Studies show that of those oldsters who are incapacitated, some 80 to 90 percent of their care is provided by members of their own family. Even when parents are healthy and do not live in the same household as their children, visitation by their children occurs several times a week, except where long distances interfere. That shows a record of commitment and responsibility. Yet there are exceptions. As one glib and articulate grandmother said, "One mother can take care of six children, but six children can't take care of one mother."

Unfortunately, our society has become more complex and more mobile, and inflation has eaten into the savings of many senior citizens who thought they had adequately planned for their own independent future. As a result, many of today's elderly are dissatisfied with, if not hostile to, what they see is going on around them. Some face severe, almost insolvable problems. At times their children, preoccupied with their own lives, fail to recognize or understand their parents' plight. But this is usually not intentional neglect. Rather, it results from an understandable ignorance or unfamiliarity with the needs of the elderly and the care that they require. But this is not surprising. There are too few teachers. Unfortunately, many physicians and other health care professionals who should lead the way do not themselves know how to handle the elderly properly, and most of the people who have learned by doing lack a platform from which to share their experiences. Our national value system seems to revere youth and shun old age. But I think that is changing. It is not reversing, but a better balance is being struck, and the next few years should bring us hope.

Yet, we must be realistic. As much as we might wish it otherwise, there are many problems in getting old. It has been said that aging is the ultimate form of personal pioneering, and indeed it is. You cannot do much about the aging process itself, but you can learn how to better understand your role as a loving and caring son or daughter. You can share in your parents' joy and help them in their sorrow. You can learn to control your feelings, even your anger. You can raise your tolerance to the many annoyances your parents may cause you. By reducing the isolation, the alienation, the conflicts, and the dependency, you can make your parents' journey into old age as pleasant as is humanly possible. Remember, loving and caring make everyone thrive, no matter what his or her age. No one knows when your aging parents' inner clocks will stop, but until they do, help them make every moment count, every breath worth breathing. Getting old is part of life. Help your aging parents enjoy it.

CHAPTER 3

Tomorrow Is Almost Here:

How to Prepare Your Parents— and Yourself— for Their Future

Photo courtesy of Milwaukee Journal

*I*f your father likes to read, chances are he has had his fill of newspaper and magazine articles warning him to prepare for his retirement. If your mother enjoys watching TV, chances are she has had her fill of programs on aging, illness, and nursing homes.

So where do you come in? You have two responsibilities: to know what good planning is, and then to help your parents do it. Remember, there is little time left for any procrastinator to plan adequately for tomorrow. As you learn about your parents' plans, you also receive an unexpected bonus. You prepare *yourself* for your parents' old age. If you are to assume your rightful role as teacher, monitor, and caregiver, you will have to learn how to act and react with your star pupils.

With almost two million individuals reaching their sixty-fifth birthday each year, it is obvious that all will not fit into the same mold and that all will not have the same needs, desires, or hopes for the future. In fact, there are worlds of differences, differences in financial security, social and ethnic backgrounds, marital status, work habits, health, levels of education, family support, religion, and differing preferences in respect to climate, recreation, and other personal considerations. Your parents will fall someplace along this broad spectrum of characteristics.

Unless you and your parents have been separated for a long time, you should know how they feel about each of these important variables. If not, a little closer observation or a discreet question here and there should fill in the voids. If you feel the situation warrants it, it may be necessary to have a sit-down discussion with your parents devoted entirely to how you and they are going to relate, not in minor personal matters, but in housing, finances, and future care. Your first responsibility in this process, whether done privately or in conversation with your parents, will be to evaluate their needs. What financial, psychological, health, and other requirements will either you or they consider essential or desirable? This appraisal can only be accomplished if you have facts—cold, hard facts. You cannot depend on rumor, assumption, or hunch. Find out what planning has been done and what has not. Determine the unresolved problems and how your parents expect to meet them. Do not guess—think them through. But remember, you will look like a fool if you unnecessarily butt into well-developed plans that your parents can adequately carry out without your assistance. On the other hand, you will end up the loser if you let your parents ignore all reasonable attempts at planning on the supposition that you will help them out if the going gets rough.

Once you know where they stand, you can then determine what responsibilities, if any, you will have to bear. Since the best laid plans can fall apart because of circumstances beyond anyone's control, some contingencies and opportunity for adjustments must be included in your planning.

By definition, the planning process implies that sufficient time remains to prepare for some future event. However, many couples fail to prepare for their old age by living each day to the fullest and spending each dollar to its limit. Others are too busy to plan for their future or too troubled by the pains of survival. Some face severe financial problems at the same time their adult sons and daughters become sufficiently well-off to afford the good life. In such situations, it is only natural that the children share their good fortune with their parents. If your parents are in a precarious position because they sacrificed everything to make your life the success that theirs was not, you have an even more compelling reason to become their benefactor. Either way, if you have to pick up part of the tab, you have an open-end invitation to become involved in your parents' planning for their old age.

Technically, your parents should have started planning for their future long before you were born, not when you became middle-aged. Furthermore, planning is not something they can do some evening when the family picnic is postponed because of rain. It takes time, time to talk to others who have experienced some of the pleasures and problems of old age, time to collect the necessary information, time to visit the Social Security Administration Office so that benefits can start on schedule, and time to get one's house in order.

Although the popular jargon says to "prepare for retirement," the more accurate task is to prepare for old age. Not everyone will retire, but everyone will grow old. Literature on retirement fills considerable shelf space in most bookstores and libraries. I have listed at the end of this chapter five references that I have found useful.

Information on aging is difficult to find, but a few references are available. Most publications on retirement planning are general in nature, covering every conceivable facet of the subject. A few concentrate on special features such as finances, places to live, psychological aspects, or health problems. Once you know the adequacy of your parents' planning, flip through these and other references and select one you think might be most helpful to your parents. Then, give them a copy or borrow it from the library. But go slowly with it. Sneak it in. For example, as you show it to them, say, "Look what I found! I wonder if it would be helpful. At least, it seems interesting. Do you want to take a look?" I doubt if very many parents would say, "No, I don't need that trash." They will peek at it. Even if they pick up only one new idea, the effort will be worthwhile.

But do not give it to them as a present for their sixty-fifth birthday. That is much too late, and it may even be misconstrued as a hint that you are divesting yourself of all responsibility for their future care. Yet, considering your age, there is little chance that you could show such a book to your parents much before they reach fifty-five or so. That would not be bad timing because your folks not only can sense its necessity then, but also can handle it emotionally.

The first step in planning for one's future at any age, but essential for aging parents, is the preparation of a will. Those with any sizable assets or a business to pass on to members of their family will have already settled that little bit of legal rigmarole. Because of fear of the possible high cost or lack of a clear understanding of the necessity of a will, too many others have procrastinated. Some confuse estate taxes with inheritance. While it is true that many do not own enough to pay estate taxes, everyone except the penniless, skid-row bum who just finished his last bottle of cheap wine has something to pass on in a manner of his own choosing. But a will is a very touchy subject to discuss rationally with your parents. If your father is the kind who does not like details or who does not appreciate younger people interfering in such personal matters, bringing it up may get you a pretty cold shoulder. If he is a business tycoon and you ask a question about his will at some inopportune time, he might misconstrue your motives. The ideal situation, of course, is to have your aging parents bring up the matter on their own. Wouldn't it be nice if they would take a few moments to tell you about their wills, tell you where they can be found, let you know if you are the executor, and if you are, what you should do and whom you should contact. I doubt if even the most thoughtful parent would offer many financial details at such a time, but that is not what is important. In fact, if a will were not important, I would say, "Forget it. It is none of your business." But what would happen to your mother if your father had no will? In whose name is the house? What about the car, the bank accounts, and what George Carlin calls one's "stuff." If the problem of a will seems to be swept under the rug, what should you do? Do not try the direct approach. You cannot win. Think up a better strategy. If you give your folks the book on planning, the matter of wills should be in there. Ask them if the book was helpful. Tell them you glanced at it, and it reminded you to write or update your own will. The connection might be made. Another approach might be through your mother. Start off by saying, "Hey, Mom, has Dad protected you in his will should anything happen, God forbid?" She may guess what you are up to, but at least you will appear considerate, not greedy. Another approach might be the "innocent remark" trick. Try saying, "Dad, I read the other day about how you shouldn't keep your will in a safe deposit box because it will be sealed until the tax people get around to inventorying it." You might get one of three answers: "What's it to you?"; "Gee, I didn't know that. I'll take mine out tomorrow"; or "Don't worry, I learned that years ago." Two of these answers should be reassuring. "What's it to you?" leaves you a bit in the dark, but you have the opportunity to oil the waters by saying, "I don't care, Dad. It was Mom I was thinking about."

My own father made me the executor of his estate, although I also had power of attorney during his lingering illness. With the concurrence of my brother, I spent almost everything my father had on his care. Then, when we knew that the end was just a day or so away, we quickly tallied up what we thought would be the few remaining bills and within the rules of the Internal Revenue Service put the rest into a scholarship in his name. That was an easy will to probate, but if I had not known what my role was to be, how much I had to work with, and what was closest to my father's heart, it would not have gone so well. Knowledge is important. Try to weasel out the facts if your parents are not thoughtful or wise enough to give them to you on their own.

It is said that women control most of the wealth in this country perhaps because they live longer and inherit it from their husbands. This is reason enough for your mother to have her own will. Someday she may hold the family's purse strings. An accident with essentially simultaneous deaths is another justification—remote but possible. Occasionally, we see an elderly man or woman die within days of the death of a spouse for no obvious medical reason. In such cases, there is very little time to execute a valid will.

Whereas the preparation of a will might be good planning in anticipation of death, it does not help much in making one's golden years really golden. Only adequate financial planning can do that. I will discuss certain financial issues of the elderly in Chapter 5, "Money Talks." Obviously financial planning for one's later years must begin when one first joins the work force. It should start with adequate savings and insurance and then, as time and funds permit, expand into investments and other wealth-promoting ventures. An employer-paid or a contributory retirement plan with reasonable vesting must be considered by every person when job hunting. A retirement plan is like breathing—it is essential for life. There is an equal need for the self-employed individual to plan for his or her future financial security. No one else will.

Today the national emphasis is on making tax and other concessions to workers for the accumulation of such funds, not on giving them handouts when they become elderly. Consequently, Social Security will become a base on which to build a retirement income, as it was originally conceived to be. It was never designed to be the only source of funds or to keep an individual at his or her former standard of living. Yet many think it was and now feel shortchanged when it does not. Although the years left to your parents to accumulate this needed retirement nest egg are running low, there is still some time left to put money into an Individual Retirement Account (IRA) right up to the last day they are eligible.

Again, check how well your parents have prepared for their financial future. Many people who are now approaching their retirement lived in pretty heady times. Credit and high prosperity did not foster thrift. The 1980s have shocked many into a new reality. For most, there is still time to do a little last-minute adjusting. It may mean giving up the boat, the expensive vacation, and the fancy lifestyle. Incidentally, the present state of the economy gives ample opportunity to discuss politics and financial problems with your aging parents. That could be your opening. In times of financial stress, people are more likely to discuss how the events of the world affect them than when prosperity gives them the stimulation to play their cards close to their chests. So talk about it. Do your own confessing. It will be like priming a pump. Your parents will be hard pressed to sit quietly by. You will soon discover if they have financial problems, cause for only crocodile tears, or enough funds to get by without your help. Remember, whatever their answer, it will affect you. Your financial future may rest on their answer. If the news is bad and the years short, you and your parents must hop to it and develop some reparative plan. As I said, it may require a change in lifestyle, and that will be difficult for many to accept. They will moan and groan in the foolish belief that the future can be happy and secure without sacrificing today. There are few such circumstances, although the definition of "sacrifice" will be different with each level of income. For some, missing a

movie will be a sacrifice; for others it will be the loss of a Florida condominium. You and your parents will have to make such tough
decisions—and fast.

I mentioned earlier that I had power of attorney during my father's illness. Such a legal document is particularly important when
only one of your parents is still living. It is created whenever an individual realizes that if he or she were ever to become incapacitated,
some responsible person should have the power to handle his or her
affairs. I once had an elderly neighbor, a distinguished professor in a
major university, who after losing his wife still had to care for his in-
valid mother-in-law who lived with them. As time went by, he
needed prostate surgery. Although he pumped me about medical matters before his operation, I was close enough to him to pump him
about legal matters. He was obviously financially secure, but I wanted
to know what would happen to his mother-in-law and his household
bills if he suffered some incapacitating complication during surgery. In
spite of his education and financial affluence, he had never considered
such a possibility. Since he had no relatives except an elderly sister
living out-of-state, he agreed to give his bank the power of attorney.
Fortunately, he didn't need it at the time, but it became necessary a
few years after his mother-in-law passed away, when he had to be admitted to a nursing home. Think about it. It may fit your family's
situation.

The date of your father's retirement—or, if your mother is working, the date of her projected retirement as well–is part of the planning process. By now your parents should have some idea of their employers' retirement payments. Assuming continued good health, they
should make their plans around that date, those funds, and whatever
other income they can anticipate. One cannot adequately plan, however, without first inventorying one's assets. Most of the elderly are
reassured to find they have much more than they expected. It makes
planning more fun than it otherwise might be. In the interim, a lot of
decisions will have to be made: financial, housing, post-retirement activities, plus many more. I will discuss most of these necessary decisions in subsequent chapters. The trick now is not to be surprised or
otherwise unprepared when these decisions have to be implemented.
Good planning should erase all surprises.

So far, I have stressed the mechanics of planning. That is what
most people think about and what most authors write about, but life is
more than mechanics. We feel, we love, we hate, we fear, we anticipate, and we express every possible human emotion. Therefore, the

function of planning is also to develop healthy attitudes toward retirement and old age. Surveys have discovered that most elderly consider themselves optimistic. They look at the twin events of retirement and old age as a new beginning. For a lucky few, it is just another birthday. They continue to work at the same old jobs and continue to follow the same old daily routines, and they like it that way. However, a large number of misguided souls look at retirement as if it were a slow downhill slide into a useless old age. They feel insecure and uncomfortable about growing old. They are afraid. They are concerned about losing the things they have spent a lifetime accumulating. They are worried that the comforts they enjoyed over the years will come to an end. They look to family ties more than ever before.

Good planning should help erase such fears and give them time to think and work things through. It should give them time to read the abundant literature on retirement, to explore the myriad of opportunities awaiting them in the years ahead, to learn that old age is the start of something new and wonderful, and that they will not only have their old friends but will have new ones as well.

Just as your parents must plan for their old age, so must you. One of the first lessons you will learn as a grown child of aging parents is that you will spend more of your waking hours thinking about your parents and their problems than ever before. You will also spend more hours working on their behalf. Obviously, this will vary depending on your parents' condition at the time, where you live in relation to them, whether you share the caring responsibility with other relatives or friends, or whether you carry it alone. Within these limitations, you may be called upon for a myriad of services. Here are some of the most likely.

The first might be called *crisis management*. Unless you live far away, you are liable to be called at any hour of the day or night because of some crisis or emergency at your parents' home. It could be something as insignificant as the cat getting loose or as serious as a heart attack. Take a hint from those physicians who handle many consultations by telephone. Just as they train their patients to know when they should call and when they should not, you can establish some ground rules for your parents. Frankly, many elderly people become hesitant even to call for help without first checking with their children or someone else whom they trust. Decisions come hard for many of them. Still others are telephone-happy and call anyone and everyone for any reason. If your parents are the calling types, educate them in advance whom they should call and for what. For example, for the sneaky cat a neighbor would be a better choice than you, unless you live next door. For the heart attack, have them first dial the ambulance or the rescue squad, then call you.

Depending on your parents' mental as well as visual acuity, you might want to prepare a deck of crisis information cards for their use. A card should be made for everyone they might need to call in a hurry: yourself, the police department, the fire department, the doctor, the hospital, the electric company, the plumber, the gas company, and others that may be needed. Chances are you can skip the TV repair shop. They will have that number memorized! Write these numbers on large file cards rather than on floppy, loose sheets of paper, and use a heavy black felt-tipped marker to print the letters and numbers at least one-half inch high so that they can be read easily even in poor light. Then clip them together with a snap-type paper clip or even in a ring binder. In addition to the list of phone numbers, it might be a good idea also to write what your parent is to say. For example, on the police card write "Police" and the phone number on the top line. On the lines below write, "This is Mrs. John Smith of 12 Elm Street, Apartment 6. I need help." It may sound silly now, but in times of crisis both young and old people often cannot remember their own names, let alone their addresses, or they get overly wordy and do not come quickly to the point, thereby wasting valuable time. While you are at it, place a flashlight alongside the deck of cards. They may need both at the same time.

You might also want to prepare a "leaving home" card. This would be a short tally of the things to be done before leaving home, such as checking for lighted cigarettes, the stove, the iron, lights, TV, timers, thermostat settings, doors, and windows, or other things to make the house safe while your parents are out. It is a simple device that can save a lot of worry—and trouble.

Your parents will also call on you for advice. Although these calls can become a nuisance, they also can help you keep in touch and may prevent bad decisions from being made. They can give you an opportunity to expand on the conversation to open new and necessary avenues of questioning that you might otherwise find difficult to do. They can be used to help the planning process. Even more importantly, they can feed your parents' souls. The elderly have strong family bonds. They want to keep in touch, to hear the family's gossip, and to feel that they still wield some family influence. Therefore, try to keep these channels open and active. Both you and they will be better off if you do.

Closely akin to their seeking advice will be their asking you to make decisions for them. Whereas giving advice shares responsibility, making decisions for your parents puts the full responsibility on you. Usually this degree of dependence does not show up until quite late in life, when thinking gets a bit fuzzy, and particularly after the individual has made one or two bad decisions that backfired. I know of one case in which an old gentleman tried to surprise his son's family by oiling their squeaky electric fan. He used so much oil that, when it was turned on, it splattered the new curtains. Now that was no great calamity, but he was so embarrassed by the resulting criticism that never again did he do his usual little chores around the house. He had lost his zeal for independent thinking, his zeal for making decisions on his own. He became dependent at a time when he should have been encouraged to remain independent. He might have been ripe for consultation but not for losing his ability to do things for himself.

Yet bad decisions on important matters can prove to be very costly. You can only hope that in such cases your folks will ask your advice. Think how much better it would be if, rather than hearing about it after the bill arrived, they would discuss beforehand the purchase of a new furnace that a dishonest door-to-door salesperson said they needed. Making medical decisions is perhaps the ultimate in dependency. Although your parents will likely withhold most minor medical problems from you, they will discuss such decisions as hospitalization and even choices of treatment if alternatives are presented to them. Chances are they will ultimately accept your decision. They also may give you the choice of which wheelchair or other piece of expensive medical equipment to buy, thinking that you are more familiar with such mechanical devices. As much as you value their seeking your advice, do not be too ready to make their decisions for them. The ability to decide for oneself is an important human desire that should not be taken away unless it is absolutely necessary. As I have said before and will say again, many middle-aged people have the same tendency to make decisions for their aging parents as they do for their children, yet neither profits from the experience. Serving as the devil's advocate is fine. It will help clarify the issues, but it will not deprive your parents of their power of decision.

Unless your parents still drive or have some other dependable source of transportation, you will be on first call. Within the limits imposed by your employment or family responsibilities, you will respond. Usually this will be for a short trip to the store or to the doctor's office, but occasionally it will be for a longer trip. In this latter situation, you may actually be needed for transportation, but more likely your presence will be requested because of your parents' fear of traveling alone. So just relax and think of yourself as a chauffeur and traveling companion. You cannot avoid it.

If you are the middle-aged son or daughter who lives closest geographically to your parents, you will likely also become the family chronicler. As your parents' handwriting becomes shaky and their eyes dim, you will end up with the added task of keeping the other members of your family informed. Some of this will be merely an extension of what you probably do already. However, some of it will be additive. Your parents will add their requests and you will have to keep other family members aware of the periodic health or household crises that inevitably occur. Of course, this will have its pleasurable side in uniting the family, but it still will take time.

The last and probably the least likely favor you will be called upon for is financial assistance. One of the greatest fears of most parents is that they will become a financial burden to their children. Unfortunately, for some there will be little choice; for others the need might be intermittent. Only time will tell. Your contribution may be in cash or in kind: food, free rent, a new TV, clothes, vacations, almost anything they might need or want. Unless your parents are truly affluent, prepare yourself and your budget for some expenditures on their behalf. Consider yourself lucky if it is the other way around.

Tomorrow is almost here. There was a day when you could muse, "What will I be expected to do when my folks get old?" Now you know. You are middle-aged. Your parents are aging. Just as they have to face the realities of old age, you have to face the realities of their being old. Although not totally pleasant, it is probably not as bad as either of you anticipate. Planning and knowledge of what to expect certainly should make the future easier. As we will see in the next chapter, once planning is done, it may be time for your aging parents to retire.

Collins, Thomas. *The Complete Guide to Retirement.* Englewood Cliffs, NJ: Prentice-Hall, Inc., 1970.

Comfort, Alex. *A Good Age.* New York: Crown Publishers, Inc., 1976.

Uris, Auren. *Over 50—The Definitive Guide to Retirement.* Radnor, PA: Chilton Book Co., 1979.

Willing, Jules Z. *The Reality of Retirement.* New York: William Morrow and Co., Inc., 1981.

Boyer, Richard, and David Savageau. *Places Rated Retirement Guide.* New York: Rand McNally, 1983.

CHAPTER 4

A Time
to Retire

Photo courtesy of Milwaukee Sentinel

*E*avesdrop with me for a moment on a conversation that might occur in hundreds of bars, clubs, company lunchrooms, bowling alleys, and wherever people meet and talk. Listen carefully.

"Me retire? Not on your life. It would kill me. I wouldn't know what to do with myself."

"I disagree, totally disagree! I look forward to it. I've planned for it. I've got a million things I want to do. I can hardly wait."

"You're absolutely right. I feel the same way. I look at retirement as a new beginning, a chance to do all of the things I never had the time to do before. It's like a reward and, by golly, my wife and I deserve it."

"Listen to him. What are you going to do all day, chase the little woman around the house? I'll tell you one thing. Retirement will be a hell of a lot easier on you than on her with you underfoot."

"Who says I'll be underfoot? I'll think of something to do, don't worry."

"Geez, you guys kill me, the whole lot of you. I hate the very thought of retiring, but I have no choice. In my company out you go at seventy, like it or lump it, and with a pension which ain't worth doodley-squat."

"I know. I'd feel a hell of a lot better if I knew I could make it on Social Security."

"You can't, so don't count on it. Ever think of another job?"

"At my age? Who'd have me except as a guard in some junkyard? The future scares the hell out of me. I'm not ready to be put out to pasture yet, not by a long shot."

Without being formally labeled as such, these old cronies are involved in the planning process we discussed in the last chapter. However, since retirement is such a pivotal part of an aging parent's life, and since it is not always accomplished in the best fashion and under the best of circumstances, it deserves special attention.

If your mother is a working woman, she shares many of the same mixed feelings about retirement as the men showed in their conversation, although she will express them in more feminine terms. Obviously, the fears and problems felt by career-oriented women are similar to those of their more hesitant male counterparts. On the other hand, most part-timers and those who work only to augment the family income look forward to retirement, provided, of course, there is adequate financial security. As you know, women do not really retire, they merely surrender one of their two jobs. They keep that of home-maker, although society does not officially recognize that as employment.

Married women who are full-time housewives—and most of the mothers in today's older generation are housewives—harbor a different set of hopes and fears. They worry or rejoice more in concert with their husband's feelings than with their own. Nevertheless, they too have certain concerns, but they usually hide them beneath the surface. They secretly worry about finances. They know the cost of food and the expenses of running a household better than their husbands. They wonder what their husbands will do all day. Will they stay at home, go out gallivanting, or mess up the house with all sorts of crazy projects? Will they want to pull up stakes and move? Will they pitch in and help with the housework, or will they alone enjoy the fruits and freedoms of retirement? Women are more likely to relate a forthcoming retirement to their children. Will they see them more often or less? Will they become a burden? But their most worrisome concern is the fear of being left out when the decisions on retirement are being made. Will they be able to express their own opinions and wishes? Remember, your mother will not retire just because your father does. She will still have a house to clean, meals to cook, and a family to take care of. She will still be responsible for much of the family budget. Therefore, she should participate as an equal partner in any decision on retirement. But a word of caution for you during this crucial period. Do not ignore the needs and feelings of your mother as you react to your father's retirement. It is easy to do, although neither fair nor helpful to either of them.

It is obvious that the word "retirement" conjures up different visions within different individuals, and that these visions are shaped not only by the individual's own perception but also by many external factors over which he or she has no control. At best it is a turning point, when one is forced to look backward as well as to look forward. Actually, it can be a frightening time for most parents of middle-aged sons or daughters, and consequently it can become a frightening time for the grown children themselves.

How do your parents look upon retirement if they still face that hurdle? Is their thinking rational or emotional? Who have been their teachers over the years: their parents, their fellow employees, or someone whose facts can't be trusted? Lucky indeed are those who still have the opportunity to plan for their own retirement, regardless of how distasteful it might be. If one of your parents had to forfeit this privilege early in life because of an accident, illness, encroaching technology, or even a disability received in one of our country's wars, he or she would tell you that they suffered the same problems then that now face elderly people. They had to make the same adjustments and fight the same fears. But life went on for them, and it will again for those yet to retire.

You may remember that in 1979 Congress passed a law that prohibited forced retirement for most public and private workers before the age of seventy. For a few executives in the upper income brackets, it is still sixty-five, and for some, including those in federal employment, it is determined only by one's productivity. As an example, look at Lowell Thomas, the dean of radio newscasters. He died essentially with his microphone on at the age of eighty-nine. Instead of contemplating retirement, he was planning a new radio series to be called "The Best Years." It was to focus on the accomplishments that certain individuals had made during their later years. Incidentally, he would have had no difficulty searching for material. Albert Einstein, Galileo, Isaac Newton, George Washington, Michelangelo, Franz Joseph Haydn, Arturo Toscanini, and Grandma Moses, to name just a few, all made history after they were sixty-five.

Since then, Helen Hayes, when in her eighties, chose the same title, "The Best Years," for her series of three-minute daily broadcasts over some 200 radio stations. In these short vignettes she recounts the achievements and pleasures of people over sixty-five. As she proudly states, ". . . I've discovered I'm not the only aged person who enjoys life more now than I did in my youth." Her confession should be reassuring to your parents. Let them know about it. In their own small way, they may also have a few spurts of greatness left in them.

Actually, the timing for retirement is being pulled by two opposing forces. The majority, including the younger workers themselves, urge their aging counterparts to stay on the job as long as possible, not so much for the money but for the continuing feeling of self-worth. A decreasing minority suggests, "Retire early so as to enjoy life and at the same time give the younger generation the opportunity for jobs." As it turns out, most people wait until they are well up in years before they retire. It is true that a few individuals such as airplane pilots and professional athletes retire whenever they can no longer meet the physical requirements, but such positions are few and far between. It is also true that the recent trend has been toward earlier retirement, not later, regardless of the type of employment. This is interesting because current opinion polls show that well over 90 percent of Americans agree that nobody should be forced to retire because of age alone. In fact, this is such a political issue that someday we may see additional legislation in that direction. It is also interesting to note simultaneously that only 75 percent of those who said there should be no age limit for retirement wanted to keep on working, and most of them only part-time. But do not count on these statistics to remain the same. Economic and political changes may well bring major shifts or reversals of how people think about their own and about someone else's retirement. Since at the present there is no hard and fast rule for everybody, the opportunity, actually the necessity, exists to make individual decisions. Unfortunately, for many older people decisions are hard to make. Consequently, your parents may need your help.

As you begin to determine your role in the future care of your own aging parents, it is quite appropriate for you to ask, "Is there a proper time for my parents to retire?" As I told my own father, "There is a time which is too early, a time which is too late, and a time which is just right." The goal of the game, of course, is to help your parents, particularly the breadwinner, determine when the timing for retirement is just right.

To make this decision, many factors must be considered. They include: finances, health, the desire to stop or to continue working, the type of job being performed, the kind of financial and emotional support the family might contribute, and many others. Each must be weighed and measured to make a sound decision, but let us not forget that luck as well as unforeseen factors may influence the outcome. Identifying the proper time to retire is not an exact science, but that must not deter us from trying to help our parents exert their best judgment.

If asked, a large segment of our working population would say that they have no choice as to the timing of their retirement; it is predetermined by their employer. However, if the definition of retirement is total withdrawal from the work force, that conclusion will not stand up. Many workers retire from one trade or profession because of company rules but jump right into a second career—full-time, part-time, paid, or volunteer. I will discuss these second careers in Chapter 8, "Keep 'Em Busy."

In those cases where timing is—at least in part—at the discretion of the individual, how does one evaluate the right time, considering the many variables? As I have suggested, this is not your decision, it is your parents'. Nevertheless, the subject must be raised either by you or by them. Since it can be an emotional issue, and since you may not know how your parents feel about retirement, it must be raised with extreme caution and tact. It would be best if your parents would settle the issue for you with a simple statement that they have worked it out and that everything is under control. That would free you from any further responsibility. On the other hand they may need your help yet be reluctant to ask for it, or they may hint at their need through some indirect questioning. So be alert to respond to any such signals.

If given this opportunity, you certainly do not want to lose it by not being helpful, but how do you go about it? How can you and your aging parents weigh all the variables? The best way is to do it methodically—on paper. You can serve your parents again by playing the role of devil's advocate. Together write down every conceivable factor that might be pertinent to their decision to retire, including those not only already mentioned but also all others that might be even remotely relevant. Such a list might contain a dozen or so items, in some simple situations less, but usually more. Leave plenty of space between sections in order to write down the pros and cons and the many subfactors that will certainly crop up within each category.

Let us take, for example, the financial issue since that ranks high on most people's list of priorities. You might first list all sources of income, if not to the penny, at least in round numbers. Is there a pension? How much? If your parents are unsure, have them ask their employers, who have an obligation to supply that information. How about Social Security? Any Social Security office can answer that question either in round figures or exactly, depending on the time you want to wait for the answer. How about private pension funds or one from a previous employer, in which case the money should be sitting around earning interest as it waits for your father or mother to meet the requirements for withdrawal? How about savings? What are these funds likely to yield as income in the future—a risky prophecy at best? Are both parents working? Are both retiring simultaneously? Their combined assets certainly have to be considered. Is there a possibility of a second career, and at what likely income? Do not forget the remote possibility of an inheritance; it does occur, even in old age. Are there things to sell, property or items around the house no longer needed or worth saving that can bring in additional funds? Will you or your brothers or sisters be able to contribute to your parents' support? Some may, some may not, and some may be unable to tell with certainty. At least, you and your parents will have some estimate of what they can expect to have coming in after retirement.

Next, what will be the likely expenses? List them: housing, food, taxes, insurance, transportation, debts, personal expenses, and of course some provision for unknown medical care. Add something for inflation; it will never be zero again. Try to estimate which of these expenses might go up in the future and which might go down.

Once all the financial data are recorded, review them in detail and analyze how each item might relate to the other factors listed on your paper, such as job satisfaction, health, and climate. With proper study, some indication of your folks' financial future should become clear.

Repeat the same type of analysis for every one of the factors that you and your parents listed on the original paper. Provided that the time of retirement is still flexible, the completed analysis should help your mother and father determine whether the kind of retirement they want is or is not possible and whether they should or should not retire at this time. Of equal importance will be the emergence of a list of necessary or desirable alternatives: move to smaller quarters, stay put, seek part-time employment, sell the camper, and so on.

In many middle- and upper-class families these questions will be unnecessary. In fact, the whole analysis can be dusted off with a quick, "No problem, don't worry" response. If so, consider yourself fortunate. But be careful! A "No problem" may be an erroneous translation of "I don't want to think about it." If there is any doubt about the financial stability of your parents' future, cajole them into facing reality; it will be to your advantage. After all, if this type of analysis is done poorly or is not done when it is essential that it be done, it will soon become your problem, not your parents'.

I also suggest that you and your parents make this appraisal conservatively. Too many people have made the decision to retire early because of some unstudied whim, some naive desire for self-indulgence, or another equally poor excuse. Then, when inflation, illness, or some other uncontrollable event came along, their whole dream was destroyed. In such cases, either their kids or welfare was left holding the bag. So remember, if the timing of your parents' retirement still rests in their hands, the better they make that decision, the better off both you and they will be.

As I hinted before, retirement is not necessarily a withdrawal from work. To be useful, productive, and active are human necessities, without which people dry up. Their lives, if not actually shortened, certainly are made less meaningful. I remember talking these things over with my father, who was seventy at the time. Still in good health and productive in a managerial position, he was fortunate in not having any deadline for retirement placed on him. So why did we talk? I felt that up to that time he had made a good decision to stay on the job. To have retired before then would have been too early. He was a widower and needed the stimulation. In addition, he was respected by his employer. But as we listed the factors and discussed the alternatives, we recognized certain odds against his continued employment. Would it not be better for him to retire when he was at the top of the pile rather than when he was sliding downhill? Sooner or later those around him would hope that he would leave one way or another. That would have been too late. Furthermore, it would have been devastating to such a proud man. So after fifty-two happy years with the same company, he made his move at a time that seemed just right.

In a few months he had caught all the fish he wanted to catch and had read all the books he had ever yearned to read. Time began to weigh rather heavily on his hands. Consequently, he spent long hours at our house reminiscing about my brother and me. He had a problem. We also had a problem—not because of his retirement, but because we had done inadequate planning. Fortunately, my brother came to his rescue. He had a small branch plant not too far away, so he gave Dad a small managerial job. For the next ten years he again became productive, but he was also sheltered from overpowering pressures. Of course, there came a time when he had to retire once again. Many of the same factors that had been evaluated a decade before had to be reconsidered. This time, the options were much different; they were fraught with limitations. The finality of the answer was obvious, not an entirely pleasant experience even the second time around.

When one realizes the morale boost even part-time jobs mean to retirees, it is disappointing to see such little interest in their promotion. However, this may be changing. I read a recent report about an insurance company that uses its retired employees as a labor pool when regular employees are sick or on vacation. Good for them! Actress Debbie Reynolds deplores the way we treat elderly actors and actresses. As she once said, "In England aging stars like Laurence Olivier are knighted by the Queen. Here, they're just put in a home. It's terrible." And so it is, not only for stage and screen personalities, but also for Joe, the truck driver, and Rosie, the riveter—or is it the other way around? I wonder if the casting of Katherine Hepburn and Henry Fonda in the film On Golden Pond was the result of Miss Reynolds' campaign? Later on, we will look at some of your parents' alternatives in this respect.

Perhaps the greatest help you can give your retiring parents is to assist them in developing a positive attitude toward this new experience. Place before them the many pleasures that lie ahead: the freedom to come and go as they please, greater contact with the grand-children and the rest of the family, and the opportunity to pursue new ventures. Perhaps with these points in mind my two children chipped in and surprised me with a retirement gift when I gave up my full-time responsibilities. The present was an Emperor grandfather clock kit, which I diligently assembled during those first few post-retirement months. Since then I have met a number of retirees who also have assembled such clocks, some more than one, with the same beneficial results. Ours has already become a family treasure. It helped me at a time when I needed a transitional activity; as a family we enjoy its musical chimes; and the grandchildren call it the mouse clock because as a lark I fastened a small toy mouse halfway up the front, as in the nursery rhyme. Think up your own bit of positive stimulation. Create your own family traditions or treasures. Do not let your parents' retirement pass unnoticed. Do not let time drag. Make it what it should be, an interesting and pleasurable cap to one's productive life.

Generally our culture reflects a rather negative image of retirement. We use uncomplimentary references such as "out to pasture," on the shelf," or "has beens." I belong to a little group of old friends that calls itself the "Has Beens." We retired about the same time. We meet monthly, usually at lunch, although we often go to a ballgame or a performance of some kind with our wives. But to us the label "Has Beens" is a badge of honor. No pastures for us; we are busy. We look at retirement with pleasure, as do our wives. None of us regrets his decision. Hopefully we will not be problems for our grown children. However, if we had all been forced out of our jobs, had done no planning, had no meaningful things to do after retirement, and had an inadequate income, I am not so sure the term "retirement" would appear so attractive to us or to our children.

Yes, there is a time to retire—not for you yet, but for your parents. It is a decision that will have serious impact on your entire family. So get involved as tactfully and compassionately as possible. It is a proper part of your growing responsibility for the care of your aging parents.

CHAPTER 5

Money Talks

Photo courtesy of Milwaukee Journal

One bright spring morning an elderly neighbor saw me struggling with a branch of a stately spruce tree that the winter wind and heavy snow had cracked. I was trying to splint it with a piece of wood and some electrical tape. Seeing I was having trouble with the tape, he brought me some special plastic twine. "Where'd you get this, Frank?" I asked. "Oh, I've been saving it. The nursery wraps it around Christmas trees, so I save it."

Frank is a classic example of today's aging parent. He never belonged to the throwaway generation. He grew up as your parents did, always saving for a rainy day. That generation hoarded buttons, nails, bottles, remnants, pieces of wood, string. They also saved their money. For many, it was not much by today's standards, but they gave up many luxuries in order to put aside their few pennies.

This dedication to thrift will now pay off for you and your parents in three important ways. First, your parents will probably have a little nest egg tucked away suitable to their present standard of living. Second, they will probably have no debts larger than a tab at the corner drugstore or the neighborhood tavern. Third, their needs will probably be modest, and to meet those needs they will be able to scrimp and save with a degree of equanimity few of your own generation would accept.

However, at some unexpected time your parents' frugality and your own credit card proclivity may clash and create painful and lasting conflict. The disagreement may not be over money per se, but rather over how money is spent. The argument will be conceptual, not financial. You probably believe in the good life and in enjoying the fruits of your labor as many in your generation do. On the other hand, your parents—who believe in self-restraint and thrift—may not. They may well feel that it is their parental duty to break you of your spendthrift habits. Any lack of diplomacy on either side at this crucial time, and bang, conflict will explode. Chances are you cannot stop your parents from acting like parents, so whatever compromise is required must come from you. Of course, if their criticism is valid, accept it. It may be the wisest thing you ever did. However, if your apparent extravagance does not jeopardize anyone or anything, just practice your best sleight of hand in order to reduce any appearance of frivolity. In simple terms I guess that means, "Keep your mouth shut and quit bragging!"

If criticism still persists, you may have to settle it by direct but friendly confrontation. There are times when you have to explain to your parents that you understand why they think the way they do and commend them for it. However, at the same time you must explain to them that today's standards are different from theirs, just as theirs may have been from their own parents'. Sooner or later they will have to accept the fact that you have to live your own life in accordance with the accepted standards of your own generation. Reassure them; convince them that you are not headed for disaster. However, do not stop there. Try to find out if there is some deep-seated reason for their displeasure other than the one given. It could be a fear of their own financial insecurity, an unnecessary concern about your own future, a false shame, almost anything. But unless the truth comes out, the spending conflict will continue to simmer only to boil up again and again. Turn off the heat once and for all!

At times, conflict can indeed be rooted in money matters. If either one of you is more affluent than the other, and there is little or no sharing when the need to share exists, conflict will surely develop. We see this situation less frequently than the philosophical difference because few parents wish to talk about it. The hurt tends to remain deep-seated but silent. The lack of sharing in these cases is usually not intentional. Rather it stems from either a lack of understanding of the other's financial position or the failure to discuss such matters openly and frankly. As I will repeat so often, aging parents dislike being financially dependent on their children. In fact, most would rather take money from the government than from their children should things ever deteriorate to that level. Consequently, when you are around your parents, they will go to any length to put on a good front in order to avoid any appearance of need. This places you in a difficult position: If you expose their charade, there can be embarrassment; if you do not, there can be suffering. Although it might appear to be a no-win situation, usually some solution can be found. Sometimes a direct approach will work—it did in reverse when your parents gave you your weekly allowance. Now may be the time for you to give your parents an allowance. Picking up part or all of an ongoing expense is often a more tactful way to proceed than giving cash. My brother and I did that with our father's life insurance policies. We were to be the beneficiaries, so we took over the cost of the premiums. Why not think about taking one or two financial burdens off your parents' backs, providing, of course, that such help is really necessary? Most telephone companies offer gift certificate coupons that can be used as cash when paying bills nationwide. We have used them in the past with great success. Not only are they a thoughtful way of helping someone, but they also serve as a subtle hint to keep in touch. Paying the rent or utility bills, or picking up the costs of vacations or medical care are ways of contributing to your parents' golden years without the passage of money from hand to hand. Many elderly persons even consider the cashing of a check as distasteful as your leaving a twenty-dollar bill on the dresser. So before you erroneously think that your parents have everything under control, check on them. Be observant; get the facts. Your parents should never be in need without your knowing it. By all means, consult an attorney if you plan more complicated transactions, such as purchasing their home, establishing a trust fund, or adopting other legal measures designed to assist your parents financially. But do not offer financial help when it is not needed.

Of course, the tables could be turned. You could be the one financially insecure, and your parents could be well off. The same feelings can crop up in reverse. Fortunately, the same solutions will also work in reverse. If there is love and understanding within a family, major problems should not arise. This does not mean that there will be no financial problems. It merely means that there will be financial equity at whatever economic level the total family finds itself.

At this point you might be asking yourself, "Am I really financially responsible for my parents' care?" One could argue at length about that question and not be sure of the answer. Actually statute and case law differ from state to state, and the matter is far from being settled. Whereas parental responsibility for minor-aged children has become universal, an adult's responsibility for his or her own aging parents is a concept that is just taking hold. Step by step we are beginning to see a change around the country, particularly as state and local governments try to protect themselves from conniving adults who dump the care of their parents onto the backs of the taxpayers. As one newspaper recently put it, ". . . the state is on the verge of applying in reverse the well-established principle that parents take care of their children. It is expected to propose that children of nursing home patients whose bills are paid by the government be required to share some of the costs." Increasingly we see where parents transfer all of their assets to their children so that they, now made destitute, will become eligible for public assistance. But that is not new. I remember such a case in the mid-fifties, long before Medicare and Medicaid, in which our hospital cared for such a woman. As a result, the costs of her treatment had to be borne by the other patients. Yet she lived in a fine family home furnished with valuable antiques, all of which had been legally transferred to her son. Technically, she was penniless. And who do you think her son was? He was a health administrator for the federal government! As one recent editorial said, "The public interest is not served if people who have financial resources are encouraged to give them to their children and then let everyone else's children pay for those elderly parents' nursing care."

In most cases you will know if there is such a need. If so, let it be known early that you are anxious to lend a hand, anxious to be your parents' safety net, at least, up to your ability. Should there be a need greater than you can appropriately handle, let it also be known that you will help them secure from some agency or some level of government whatever other assistance might be necessary.

If there does not appear to be any financial problem, relax and enjoy your freedom. It may not last very long.

Incidentally, I am not going to discuss welfare. Although it is perhaps pertinent to this chapter on money, most of you will not have parents in that economic bracket. Nevertheless, I wish our society would look at welfare as a respectable way of temporarily sheltering the shorn lamb from the wind. There are times when hard-working, contributing citizens suffer tragedies that are almost impossible to imagine. Some are temporary, some permanent. We see them in medicine every day. Yet rarely does society come to the rescue of these poor souls; rarely do they apply for assistance because they are not truly destitute. We have grown up thinking that welfare is primarily a system of continuing support for generation upon generation of chronically disadvantaged individuals. It would be nice if some system could be devised whereby productive souls temporarily down on their luck but not impoverished could also be given a helping hand, but we all know that such a system could not be operated without red tape, injustice, and fraud. What does this mean for you? It means that under most circumstances you are the only source of emergency assistance your parents can expect when they have a temporary spot of bad luck. However, I suggest you do not completely forget welfare. It might be a last resort when all other financial resources are gone.

I also am not going to discuss specific investments and other matters of financial planning. They are not appropriate to my primary purpose of helping you with the care of your aging parents. Nor am I going to quote dollar values of Social Security or other government benefits. They change with the whim of Congress. In case you do not believe me, consider what a federal pamphlet printed in 1935 stated about Social Security: ". . . beginning in 1947, twelve years from now, you and your employer will each pay 3 cents on each dollar you earn, up to $3,000 a year. This is the most you will ever pay." See why I don't clutter up these pages with current government figures? They are as changeable as the next election.

But I am going to discuss your parents and their money. If they are typical, both their income and their expenses should decrease with retirement. If they are lucky, and if they did some thoughtful financial planning about thirty years ago, the odds are that they will be able to get by. The stereotype of the senior citizen is one of limited means if not abject poverty. It reeks of thrift-shop clothing, sunken cheeks, and lost hope. Don't believe it! A 1981 Louis Harris Poll showed that 68 percent of those under sixty-five years of age thought that finances were a serious concern for the elderly. However, when he asked those over sixty-five, only 17 percent thought so. Actually, only 6 percent of the elderly live at or below the established poverty level. The rest, if not wealthy, are at least comfortable. Statistics show that although those over fifty-five currently make up only 20 percent of the population, they control 28 percent of the country's discretionary income. By the year 2000, their share of the nation's wealth will substantially increase by virtue of the aging of our population. What is more, we are now beginning to see a narrowing of the wide chasm between the thrifty generation of yesteryear and the credit card generation of today. Some of the young-olds have learned a few new tricks from the "me" generation. They are beginning to enjoy their money, and their compulsion to save as much as they can is fading. They have lost much of their former caution and penny-pinching, and they have moved into the mainstream. Indeed, the elderly are big spenders, as we shall see later in this chapter.

It is different with the old-olds. They have not been as flexible. Perhaps this is because they have had fewer funds to work with. The young-olds experienced a period of midlife prosperity that gave them a financial edge over their older associates who were at their earning peak in the earlier lean years. Consequently, if your parents are only now entering old age, caring for them in the future might be different from that which will be required if they are already well up in years. I would imagine that if comparative figures for the percentage of discretionary income available between those over sixty-five and those over seventy-five were published, the amounts would be proportionately reduced for the old-olds. Nevertheless, your parents' financial position relative to their peers, younger or older, will depend more on the national economy and their expenditures for health care than on the timing of their retirement. Where your parents fall on this income and spending scale, and how that might influence the care you will need to give, can be determined only by them and you.

It is not surprising to learn that the greatest financial concern of every senior citizen, except for the very extremes on the economic spectrum, is the unknown cost of health care. The very rich have the resources to take care of themselves; the very poor have the government. Neither has much to worry about. Unfortunately, everybody in between knows that a long illness could wipe them out. But you ask, "Doesn't Medicare take care of that?" Well, in part it does—but only in part. Here is how it works.

Everyone sixty-five or older who is entitled to monthly Social Security or Railroad Retirement benefits automatically receives hospital insurance (Medicare Part A) without cost, regardless of whether he or she is still working. If your parents are sixty-five or over and have not contributed to Social Security or Railroad Retirement or have not contributed to Social Security long enough to be eligible for retirement benefits, they can still buy Medicare coverage much as they would any other health insurance. Although Medicare has its limitations in benefits and payments, it is still the biggest bargain for any elderly individual not automatically covered.

In addition to the hospital insurance benefits (Medicare Part A) your parents are eligible for certain medical benefits (Medicare Part B). This package covers visits to the doctor and certain outpatient, home health, and rehabilitative services. Your parents become eligible for this optional coverage when they join Medicare, but they are charged an additional monthly premium. Although Part B, like Part A, has certain limitations in benefits and payments, it is also a bargain and should not be passed up when applying for basic Part A Medicare. The range of services covered by Part B and the monthly charges are established by Congress and, therefore, can be changed by Congress at any time. Your parents' local Social Security office can advise them of the current costs and list of benefits.

It is likely that your parents have been so blasted by the media and their peers that they have taken advantage of these favorable federal programs. But do not take it for granted—check! A busy, healthy parent of sixty-four years and nine months may not have this on his or her mind, and the oversight could be costly. Note that I said sixty-four and nine months, not sixty-five, because application for both Social Security and Medicare should be made approximately three months in advance of one's sixty-fifth birthday. If your parents are retired civil service employees, veterans with service-connected disabilities, or members of the railroad retirement system, they most likely have been fully informed of the special benefits due them.

Few people but the elderly know that on the average Medicare covers slightly less than 40 percent of their total health care expenses. Actually, the percentage is going down, not up as many people had expected. The health care costs not covered by Medicare include routine physical exams, drugs, eyeglasses, dental care, hearing aids, immunizations, cosmetic surgery, private rooms in a hospital, care in a nursing home at a custodial level and many other expenses, all listed in the Social Security Administration's booklet entitled "Your Medicare Handbook."

Fortunately, the financial risk of such uncovered expenses can be reduced by the purchase of supplemental health care insurance, but the premiums are significant. This does not infer that the high cost of health care can be forgotten because insurance is available. Quite to the contrary, the public must remain concerned about these high costs. Fortunately, much is being done on many fronts, and many previously untouchable practices are beginning to be touched. The federal government had been tinkering with the cost of health care for the elderly long before Medicare became available in 1965, but it had never hit the bull's eye. I have always wondered why not. Most of the legislators were in the right age group or had parents in the right age group, but I guess they did not sense the economic hardships acutely enough to tackle the problem with sufficient gusto. Furthermore, we assume we live in a democracy responsive to the needs of the majority, but this is not so. We live in what I like to call a "balpresgracy," a system of government characterized by a *bal*ance of *pres*sure *g*roups. Although that balance of power has tried to handle health care costs, there have remained enough loopholes to permit all sorts of people to take advantage of the system. That has been unfortunate, because in many ways it has caused the system to lose credibility. I cannot say what the next generation of legislators will do, but I will guarantee you that they will continue to tinker with the problems of health care without solving them. Again, we will see balpresgracy in action.

I have no foolproof recommendations to offer in respect to your parents' health care costs, but I think improvemens will come by evolution of the present system, not by some sweeping piece of legislation. Actually, that is a slow but sound way to make progress. The federal government will have to set standards and see that the health care industry observes those standards. But no proposal will be successful unless government and every other segment of society work together. That is beginning to happen.

Hospitals are now under the gun to control costs. Certainly they will never go back to the time when they balanced their budgets on the backs of low-paid workers or out of the pockets of wealthy contributors. Nor will they voluntarily ration health care or cut its quality in order to reduce costs. Management and patient-care techniques will become more efficient; waste will be reduced; competition will creep into the system. Costs will not go down, but you and your parents will, at least, get your money's worth. As time goes by, inefficient hospitals will fall by the wayside. If this means that your parents will have to travel farther for their medical care, so be it!

Physicians will also get into this act. Those who abuse the system or the public trust will have their privileges removed. Self-regulation will be strengthened. After a decade or more of working with Medicare, most physicians are beginning to recognize the financial pinch many of their elderly patients are experiencing. Consequently, all around the country physicians are again adjusting their fees to their patients' financial abilities. I recently saw a headline in the *Wall Street Journal* that said "Strange but True: Doctors Cutting Rates for Elderly, Idea Catches On." Hopefully as a society we will continue to improve the quality of health care as we simultaneously keep its cost within the reach of those who need it. However, this cannot be done unless the public keeps the pressure on the government, on hospitals, on physicians, and on the whole health care industry, including the unions and suppliers. They must also put pressure on themselves. The elderly as well as all Americans must learn to accept a lifestyle that will prevent illness, must learn to use medical facilities wisely, and must learn that they will have to do more for themselves rather than having simple services done by expensive employees.

As we all know, the elderly use health care facilities more than any other segment of our population. Since that care is so expensive, they are very concerned about its costs, and since health insurance is one way to shelter oneself from these high costs, the elderly eagerly buy health insurance. All of these things are understandable. But what is not understandable is why they buy every cockamamie policy they see advertised. In this age of computers, some data bank has probably tipped off one or more health insurance carriers that your parents have reached the age where they will need some sort of health insurance to supplement Medicare. This type of coverage pays for what Medicare approves but does not pay for. If your parents' former employer does not offer such additional protection after retirement—

and few do—your parents should give it serious consideration. It may be expensive, but if you tally the odds of needing it, it soon becomes indispensable. However, as you might guess, there are a lot of policies that are not smart buys. Generally, we in medicine discourage policies that apply to a specific disease such as cancer, diabetes, or heart attack. Illnesses usually do not come in such neat packages. We also caution against ridiculously cheap policies loaded with restrictions which pay out such small sums that they are essentially useless in today's market. Therefore, if necessary, help your parents through the confusing maze of insurance language. Many policies are not what they first appear to be. If you or your parents have a problem in understanding the fine print, consult the consumer protection agency in your area or the State Insurance Commissioner's office. Both usually rate various policies on some objective scale.

I have never seen any statistics on the dollar volume of the medical benefits that the elderly are due but for many reasons never collect. It must be enormous. A large part of the problem is the complexity of the claim process. Frankly, almost everyone including my wife and myself has a difficult time keeping track of insurance claims and payments. If you have any talent for setting up simple financial records and your parents need help, go to it. A shoebox in the hall closet stuffed with insurance records is not enough.

Although my wife and I only have Medicare and a Medicare supplemental policy to worry about, we had to develop a system that would keep us informed as to where we stood in this health insurance business. We now keep a set of records with, believe it or not, eleven columns. From left to right they are:

1. Date
2. Service rendered
3. Total amount charged
4. Amount we, hospital, or doctor billed directly to Medicare
5. Amount approved by Medicare before co-insurance reduction
6. Amount Medicare applied to the deductible
7. Amount paid by Medicare
8. Amount billed to Medicare supplemental insurance
9. Amount Medicare supplemental insurance applied to the deductible
10. Amount Medicare supplemental insurance paid
11. Amount that was not reimbursed and, therefore, we paid (see Figure 1)

Name *Lorna Hilyard* Year 1984 Page 1

DATE	SERVICE RENDERED	Total Charges	Billed to Medicare	Approved by Medicare	Applied to Deductible	Paid by Medicare	Billed to Supplemental Insurance	Applied to Deductible	Paid by Supplemental Insurance	Self Pay
Mar. 4	Office visit, Dr. Handy, flu	18.00	18.00	16.00	16.00[1]	-0-	18.00	16.00[2]	-0-	18.00
Mar. 7–11	Anytown General Hospital, pneumonia	1,586.00	1,586.00	1,586.00	N/A	1,230.00[3]	356.00	84.00 / 100.00	272.00	84.00
Mar. 7–11	Hospital visits, Dr. Handy	60.00	60.00	40.00	40.00	-0-	60.00	-0-	40.00	20.00[4]
Mar. 18	Office visit, Dr. Handy—follow-up on pneumonia	18.00	18.00	16.00	16.00	-0-	18.00	-0-	16.00	2.00
	—chest X-ray / —blood count	52.50	52.50	43.00	3.00 / 75.00	32.00[1]	52.50	-0-	11.00	9.50
Aug. 16	Office visit, Dr. Handy, high blood pressure	18.00	18.00	16.00	-0-	12.80	18.00	-0-	3.20	2.00
Aug. 16	Prescription #409063	11.85	(not covered by Medicare)				11.85	-0-	11.85	-0-
Nov. 2	Office visit, Dr. Lenz—eye exam	12.00	12.00	12.00	-0-	9.60	12.00	-0-	2.40	-0-
	—refraction for glasses	10.00	(not covered by Medicare or Supplemental)							10.00
Nov. 3	Eyeglasses—City Optical	96.00	(not covered by Medicare or Supplemental)							96.00
		1,882.35								241.50

EXPLANATION

[1] IN 1984 MEDICARE PART B PAID 80% OF APPROVED CHARGES AFTER $75 DEDUCTIBLE
[2] SUPPLEMENTAL POLICY PAID WHAT MEDICARE PARTS A AND B APPROVED BUT DIDN'T PAY AFTER $100 DEDUCTIBLE
[3] IN 1984 MEDICARE PART A INPATIENT DEDUCTIBLE WAS $356 FOR EVERY BENEFIT PERIOD
[4] ASSUMES PHYSICIAN DOES NOT ACCEPT AS FULL PAYMENT WHAT MEDICARE OR INSURANCE PAYS
N/A NOT APPLICABLE—INPATIENT DEDUCTIBLE NOT PART OF MEDICARE PART B DEDUCTIBLE
NOTE: MEDICARE SUPPLEMENTAL POLICIES MAY VARY IN BENEFITS OFFERED.

R. R. Cadmus, 1984

Figure 1

If your folks have more than one Medicare supplemental policy, there must be additional columns for each one. Parts A and B of Medicare also have to be kept separate by additional columns, separate sheets, or appropriate notations in the "service rendered" column. We keep a separate record for each of us, and we start a file each calendar year. Unfortunately, the time between receiving service and receiving payment may run over many months. Unless your parents have records, they will be lost in the jungle of paperwork. Of course, they will have to keep in some orderly fashion the numerous bills, explanation of benefit forms, check stubs, and other back-up materials that flood the mails. Since no one can remember which services are covered, it is wise to keep with these financial records current copies of the insurance booklets that outline the services covered. Now, that's a hefty piece of recordkeeping for an ordinary senior citizen. But unless your parents keep records like this, they will never keep track of what they claimed, what they received, and what could be counted as unreimbursed medical expenses at tax time. If the payments fall short of what is anticipated, suggest to your parents that they query the proper claims office. They do make mistakes, but unless your parents squawk, no correction will be forthcoming.

As I indicated earlier, some old people can be made destitute in spite of Medicare and Medicare supplemental insurance. This usually occurs to those with long-term illnesses, when either Medicare benefits run out or the patient requires services not covered by Medicare (particularly nursing home care at a custodial, not a skilled level). Furthermore, most insurance policies today carry "medical necessity" clauses which mean that coverage is extended only to those days of care in a hospital or to those services out of the hospital which are medically necessary, not to those which may be desirable or required by social problems at home. If one spouse should run up such unreimbursed bills, the other could soon be left destitute. This is a chilling thought to any marriage partner. The present rules for most county or state medical assistance programs require the beneficiary to have essentially no assets except for a few personal belongings. Their house is lost, perhaps last, but if necessary, it goes. What will happen to the spouse? Where will he or she go? In some areas there are lien programs designed to protect the individual's homestead during his or her lifetime. A few other innovative solutions have been developed around the country, but none are very comforting. The fact that we do not read about such sad cases in the local press is not because they do not occur, but rather because, as I said earlier, the generation of elderly people getting along on their own do not seem to sell very many newspapers. But before I leave the subject of financial pressures on the aged, let me compliment the vast majority of middle-aged people who, when necessary, unselfishly contribute to their parents' financial security. They have come through with no fanfare, no publicity, just generosity motivated by love and understanding.

Although inflation has come under some control and has disappeared from the headlines, its damage is still being felt. Inflation has been cruel to your parents' generation. In 1952 I did my first real financial planning. A very competent advisor outlined a program for me designed to yield about $4,800 per year which, with Social Security, was estimated to provide a modest but acceptable retirement income in the university community in which I lived. Actually, it was not bad planning considering that hospital costs were running at about $16 per day, and everything else was proportionately priced. Obviously, inflation ruined that plan. Your parents suffered the same deterioration of the plans they had for you, for their grandchildren, and, of course, for their own future. I saw an editorial cartoon the other day in which the first panel showed the opportunities for retirement income available to executives, professionals, and politicians, and the second panel showed a blue-collar worker asking "What about me?" That's a good question! Many people of modest means have not had the financial opportunity to prepare adequately for their retirement. Inflation hit them with a blow from which they have never fully recovered. This may be the reason why your father is still working either at his old job or one of less stature, or why your mother still works as a seamstress or baby-sitter. Have you ever wondered whether their continued employment is by choice or because of past inflation? It could be for either reason.

Inflation has also hit your parents with higher housing costs. This is seen not only in their rent or taxes, but also in their heating and utility bills. For most of the elderly, these increases have come at a time when they are living on relatively fixed incomes. In the snow belt regions of this country, there are often publicly supported programs to help the poor with their heating bills. Such benefits, however, are not available to families with modest incomes. Yet I constantly hear many elderly complain that they have saved and scrimped all their lives only to find out that they are now taxed additional amounts to heat the homes of those who in their earlier years enjoyed big cars and high living.

These increases in taxes and utility bills may force your parents to consider reductions in other areas, such as food, health care, clothing, and recreation. Unfortunately, priorities can soon become misplaced because, except for some conservation of energy, the cost of housing is a fixed part of their family budget. Fortunately, there are some alternatives. Many of my contemporaries are moving to smaller quarters partly because of cost but partly because of convenience. If your parents are toying with such a move, you probably will be informed if not involved. Actually, it might be wise for you to take the initiative, particularly if it makes good financial sense, because such a possibility might not have occurred to them, or they might so dread the thought of it that they have shut it out of their minds. Do not underestimate the emotional pull of the old homestead or the headaches of moving. I will discuss housing in more detail in Chapter 6, "Home Sweet Home." However, at this point you must remember that the costs of housing can put a severe financial strain on your parents. On the other hand, you must also recognize that the sale of the homestead might stop their financial hemorrhage, provided of course less expensive housing is available. You may not be faced with such a problem with your parents, but if you suspect that something like this might exist, see if you can help.

Your parents can squeak by on reduced expenditures for clothing, transportation, and recreation but not to any great extent for food. Here again, I will go into more detail in Chapter 12, "They Are What They Eat," but for now let me emphasize the direct relationship between money and food and between food and health. Cutting back on nutrition is one of the first actions most elderly take when money gets tight. However, the short-term effects are not very apparent, because hunger will either pass or can be satiated by foods high in starch, fat, or bulk. The long-term effects, however, can be devastating. Vitamins are lost, body fat either wastes away or accumulates abnormally, bones become softened, nutrients for strong red cell replacement and for tissue repair are lacking, the immune system is starved, and the individual is exposed to all the health problems associated with malnutrition. Any intercurrent disease or infection can overwhelm such a debilitated individual. Many elderly unfamiliar with the aging process will falsely assign the signs and symptoms of malnutrition to normal old age. Neither you nor they may make the connection. Obviously, good nutrition should not be confused with gourmet dining—there is a difference. Unfortunately, good nutrition is not cheap in today's market. Starches and animal fats may be inexpensive and may even help put on weight, but alone they do not constitute a balanced diet. In times of financial stress, do not let adequate nutrition go by the boards. It is a dangerous game.

You will recall that I mentioned earlier that not all elderly are financially strapped but, in fact, may be big spenders. The proof of this is the enthusiasm with which advertisers go after the older consumer. The over-55 market is big business. Not only is that segment of our population expanding, but it also controls about $350 billion in disposable annual income. Your parents are part of that market. Once you and your brothers and sisters flew the coop, your parents had more money to spend on themselves, and the vendors knew it. They began to publish magazines catering to their interests. The cosmetic industry responded by offering products designed to make the elderly woman look younger. The chewing gum manufacturers developed gum that will not stick to dentures. I never thought I would see disposable diapers for adults advertised on TV, but now I do along with insulin syringes, denture creams, hemorrhoidal remedies, drugs for constipation, products for diarrhea, hair dyes, foot care supplies, arthritis rubs, and dozens of other things the elderly need and use. New TV programs address themselves to the senior citizen, the excellent "Over Easy" program being only one example. Banks, mortgage lenders, and brokers of all kinds recognize the nest eggs people like your aging parents have stashed away, and they do their best to get their hands on them. Senior citizens are travel bugs. Just ask any travel agent or look in the waiting room of any airport. On the other hand, the gold and silver buyers offer cash for the outdated, broken, or unwanted pieces of jewelry, flatware, or decorator items tucked away in the homes of the elderly. I even read one research report that showed that older adults consume more sweets than young people. Apparently that age group remembers that during the Depression in the thirties sweets were a rare treat, and they continued the craving. Now I know why I like sweets! How about some fruit instead?

Akin to creating products for the elderly, the practice of offering them discounts is becoming almost universal. Although this is usually an individual matter with each shopkeeper, in some metropolitan areas there are organized programs for enlisting establishments that grant discounts. Verification of age varies from special senior citizen cards to the use of driver's licenses, although I have noticed that very few shopkeepers request such proof. Discount cards for various establishments are often passed out at senior citizen meetings or senior centers. We use them—why not? It's not charity. The proprietor wants to increase his or her volume of sales and is willing to shave the profit to get the business. So we help the shopkeeper. I hope your aging parents do too. Every little bit counts!

Many of these discounts are available only at off-peak hours. For most seniors, this is not a penalty. They avoid the crowds, the tight parking, the rowdy celebrants, and everything else most elderly prefer to stay away from. What is more, they can enjoy their pleasures without driving in the dark. If your parents do not drive, they may be able to take advantage of the discounts on public transportation during the same off-peak hours.

Finally, I must add a painful postscript to this subject of money and old people. As I trust you realize, crooks and con artists abound, trying by every means possible to illegally separate your parents from their money. Their scams, bait-and-switch schemes, and shoddy practices are legion. However, their success depends upon two human foibles: greed and ignorance. I don't know why old people, who have long known there is no free lunch, believe there can be one in their golden years, but they do. Obviously, this does not happen to those with adequate funds, but works only with those who are financially desperate. Gullibility and ignorance are another matter. With all the publicity about such rackets, it is amazing how many old people escape the lesson. If your parents are in that susceptible group, warn them, teach them, remove the need for greed. It is a tragic scene!

I trust this recitation has proved to you that money talks, particularly in the lives of your aging parents. But it also talks to you. If you are one of those who has to contribute financially to your parents' support, I urge you to keep good records. Under certain circumstances, these expenditures can be deductible on your income tax return. Those who have been contributing this way for a number of years can repeat the Internal Revenue Service's regulations verbatim. However, each year many middle-aged children will face this possibility for the first time, and the following April they will try to reconstruct some of the figures needed for the IRS. Usually they will fail. Therefore, whenever you see that you are beginning to put large sums into the support of your parents, keep records. It will prevent you from premature gray hair!

In any industrial society, money talks. How much your parents will enjoy their old age and how much you will have to put into their care will, in part, depend on how much money they have available. I hope it will be enough.

CHAPTER 6

Home
Sweet
Home

Some 160 years ago John Howard Payne wrote an opera that contained the famous line, "Be it ever so humble, there's no place like home." Your aging parents will echo that simple statement as if it were their own. Wherever and whatever they call home, there will be no place like it. Both their hearts and their hats will rest there. It will shelter their roots and feed their memories. Yet sadly and reluctantly, many elderly individuals will be forced to leave it long before they are ready.

In this chapter I cover the housing alternatives your parents might consider if they are relatively mobile and self-sufficient. In Chapter 13, "Homes Away From Home," I will discuss those facilities in which they may be housed, temporarily or permanently, if they become ill or disabled.

"But what," you may ask, "does housing have to do with caring for your aging parents?" You may not be intimately involved in what they do within their home or where they place the furniture, but you will be involved if they ever move from it. In the meantime, your role will be different, depending on where your parents live, with whom they live, and how well they live. Like it or not, you will be involved in their housing.

The following outline suggests some of the many alternate living arrangements available to your parents:

I. Living in Their Own Home
   A. Close to family
   B. Distant from family
   C. Home equity-conversion

II. Living with Family
   A. With one of their children
      1. Within child's home
      2. In separate apartment
   B. With other relatives

III. Living with Others
   A. As a tenant
   B. In shared housing

IV. Living in an Institution
  A. Custodial care
  B. Retirement facility
    1. Housing only
    2. Comprehensive care

V. Wandering about
  A. Essentially homeless
  B. Motor home or yacht

It is obvious that during your parents' later years they may live in a number of such settings depending on their needs and the circumstances at the time. Although a few, usually affluent retirees move to some resort area or to a distant location of their own choosing, most senior citizens move for some reason bordering on sad necessity, not free choice. Deterioration of their health or deterioration of their homestead are the two main reasons for their forced relocation. You may have noted that simple truth from watching the comings and goings within your own neighborhood.

If upon retirement your parents are considering some exotic move to revel in some dream or fantasy, suggest that they carefully consider all facets of such a move. Urge them to talk to those who have followed that route before, to make a trial visit to the place or facility, or to go by their local library and read books on retirement living. Although their relocation might be considered a part of caring for your aging parents, it is a separate subject that I shall pass with only this warning: Many senior citizens with stars in their eyes have made grievous mistakes; help your parents avoid any such decision. In the process, remember what I have said about isolation. Places are just places, but family and friends are one's lifeblood.

Given good health, most older people would prefer to stay where they are, provided, of course, the facilities meet their needs. In most cases, they are comfortable. They have their friends and a host of familiar social contacts. Furthermore, they may well remember the backbreaking hassles of moving. But if their health fails, the comfortable becomes uncomfortable; the secure, insecure. At that time, both you and and they will agree that it would be better if they either lived closer to you or in one of the more acceptable alternatives available to them.

As I indicated earlier, at times the homestead will no longer meet their needs. It may be too large to handle, the upkeep may be too expensive, the neighborhood may have changed, or the climate may no longer seem as hospitable as it once did. Although moves for these reasons may be thoughtfully planned, they are not necessarily filled with joy. Old roots are hard to cut off and new anxieties materialize like summer storms. It is not the best of times for your parents. The emotional as well as the physical stress can be threatening. You can expect sadness, you can only hope that they will avoid illness.

Whether or not you are present during their move is perhaps a personal matter dictated by circumstances at your end as well as at theirs. Your presence may help, but on the other hand it may interfere. Being with your parents from start to finish during any move certainly can be very supportive. There will be chores to do, errands to run, and even tears to dry. Yet there may be times when your parents would prefer to be alone, to do things by themselves at their own pace. Furthermore, helping them pack certain personal belongings can be an unwelcomed intrusion into their privacy. They may not want to make decisions as fast as you might urge them. They may want to reminisce, to savor the past, to enjoy together the last few moments. If they want to be alone, let them. It is their move.

At other times you may be torn between being with them when they leave the old place or being able to greet them at the new. It is my personal opinion that you will be needed at the new location more than at the old, not just to work but to give it the friendly feeling of home. Of course, if the move involves only a remaining spouse, your presence throughout the whole ordeal may make the difference between whether the job gets done or not. But whatever you do, do it with some degree of thoughtful planning and mutual agreement. Do not just pop in and out at your own convenience. That is not what I call caring.

For many oldsters, the move will be no big deal. They have done it before, and they are emotionally and physically able to do it again. The move may even be anticipated with a certain amount of pleasure. So be guided by the individual circumstances, but take warning. Conflict can spring up, particularly if your folks need you during their move and you are not there. They may be too self-centered at the time to understand your perfectly good excuse. They may be sufficiently upset to twist your valid absence into something resembling abandonment. Don't add conflict to an already bad situation.

To understand the impact each of these possible living arrangements might have on you and your parents, let us go through them one at a time.

Living in Their Own Home

It will make a considerable difference to you if your parents live near you or far away. Actually, there are advantages as well as disadvantages in both arrangements. Proximity permits certain sharing and easy communication, but it also can promote meddling and unnecessary involvement in each other's lives. Distance, on the other hand, leads to greater independence for each party but higher costs of getting together. It would be sad if there were little or no communication between you and your parents, because it would indicate a deep-seated conflict of some sort or, at least, an uncaring attitude on your part. Not long ago I was speaking to a group of eighth graders about aging when one of the youngsters confessed that her family rarely visited her out-of-state grandparents because, when they did, all her parents and grandparents did was fight. Obviously, I do not know the details, but I do know that distance played a factor in their relationship. Perhaps the friction exists because they do not visit often enough. Perhaps it is because of some longstanding family squabble and the distance makes the situation tolerable for both parties—at least, most of the time. I doubt if that family would ever choose the second alternative, nor would I recommend it.

In most cases, however, love, respect, and caring for one another can overcome distance. A location nearby need not be better than one far away. Some would prefer one, some the other. So be it! But whether far or near, make the relationship as meaningful and as happy as the circumstances permit.

With increasing frequency, we are beginning to see parents who are abandoning their own homes, primarily because of financial pressures. These old people are in good health, love their homes, and would prefer to stay put, but the upkeep, taxes, utilities, repairs, and maintenance take too much of a bite from their limited incomes for them to survive adequately. Fortunately, there is now a new and rather innovative solution for such cases. It is called *the home equity conversion plan*. It is open to homeowners sixty-five years of age and older. Under this system a bank, savings and loan association, or even a unit of government agrees under contract to pay the owner a monthly allowance. When the house is sold, the investor collects the full amount he or she has paid out, interest at a rate agreed to in advance, and a percentage of any appreciation the house may have undergone during the life of the contract. Such a conversion plan can be a valuable income source for the elderly homeowner. It should also interest you not only because you are concerned with your parents' happiness, but also because in due time you might be an heir to their estate. Of course, the real effect on your inheritance cannot be predicted because of the unknown longevity of your parents. The longer your parents occupy the homestead, the less equity there would be in the eventual liquidation. But you may not have much choice; it might come down to either sharing some of their expenses now so that they might continue to enjoy their home, or having them put it under such a plan and not inheriting much later on.

Hopefully, the decision would not be made entirely on monetary grounds. Any such consideration should involve feelings as well as finances. I suppose technically it is none of your business what your parents do with their own house; they can do with it anything they jolly well wish, and indeed some will. Most parents, however, will discuss such a dilemma with their children, but if you suspect a problem, do not wait until it blows sky high. If you really care about your parents, you should be sensitive enough to their needs and lifestyle to recognize any difficulties before they have to bring them to your attention. But regardless of who mentions it first, review the many alternatives discussed here with your parents. It might result in a better selection.

Living with Family

Your life will be considerably altered if your parents move from a distant homestead either into your home or into one that is very close, let us say within easy walking distance. In either situation, the two families will become essentially one. Should that distance lengthen so that it would take a car or public transportation to get from one house to the other, it would no longer be classified as an extended family which, if you remember, is defined as children, parents, and grandparents living either under the same roof or so close to one another as to permit constant contact.

The extended family, the way most families used to live before we became a mobile society, offers both your children and your parents many enriching experiences. It also offers the unpleasant possibility of conflict arising from unresolved incompatibilities. Scientists have discovered that overcrowding in rat populations causes them to develop combative behavior. The same can be said for humans. The more people one squeezes into a single household, the greater the odds are for interpersonal conflicts. But this should not be taken as a criticism against an extended family. Quite to the contrary, it merely raises a caution flag. Caring for your aging parents in your own home is more difficult, but more loving, than if they lived in any of the other alternatives, and I think we will see the return of many extended families as this nation evaluates its priorities. Nevertheless, let me add one small disclaimer. Although I personally know of no situation where parents from both sides of the family live under the same roof, I would discourage it. That would be just too many people for one average family to assimilate.

If your parents live with one of your siblings or with another relative, the relationship between you and them will be dictated more by distance than by any other factor. Actually, it will be much the same as if they were living in their own home located some distance away. If they happen to live close by, the relationship might roughly approximate the extended family. If they happen to live a great distance from you, the contacts will naturally thin out. Unfortunately, there is a strong tendency under such circumstances to pass the buck, to let some other member of the family take the responsibility. Although I do not like the rotation of parents between siblings on some arbitrary basis, like a month here and a month there, visitation is desirable for every family member. It gives your parents a welcome change, gives your siblings a respite from their daily responsibility, and gives you and your family the opportunity to share in their care. Financial participation is, of course, variable depending on the needs and assets of each member, but just because your parents are living with someone else, it does not mean that the financial burden should not be equitably divided.

In Chapter 17, "Three Ways to Cope," I will discuss in considerable detail the physical arrangements that you and your siblings should make in your homes in order to house your parents properly when they are ill or disabled and require special care. However, if you adopt these same suggestions when your parents are still spry and self-sufficient, they will also serve admirably if and when their health so deteriorates that more care is required than you originally anticipated.

As you will learn, a perfect solution to the housing needs of your parents living in your home or in the home of one of your brothers or sisters will be hard to come by. Usually some compromise is required. However, two helpful suggestions that come close to a perfect solution should be mentioned. The first is a separate but attached unit either in the form of a duplex or an attached apartment that your parents could occupy. Actually, the construction of a small apartment connected to your own home is often a sound investment. If designed properly, such an addition can serve a number of useful purposes in the future, such as a source of rental income, a master bedroom suite, a guest apartment, an office, or even servant's quarters (although this is less likely in most households today).

The second, more innovative solution, but one that may run afoul of some zoning laws, is the placement of a mobile home in your back- or sideyard. These units, sometimes called *granny homes*, provide comfortable, ready-made housing for aging parents while offering the privacy so cherished by both elderly parents and their children. If conditions permit, a covered passageway can be built connecting the two facilities. When the need is past, the unit can be sold and removed from the site, perhaps to serve the same purpose for someone else's family nearby.

Living with Others

In discussing this form of housing, I am going to assume that only one of your parents is still living and that for one reason or another the surviving parent will have to move from his or her present home. Although it is possible for a couple to enter into some shared housing arrangement, it is quite unusual. Furthermore, I hesitate to refer to the following alternatives as "living with strangers," because the people with whom your mother or father might share living quarters are often friends before the move. If not, they certainly will be as soon as the move takes place.

The first option your parent might consider is to become a tenant in someone else's home. Whether your mother or father is the only tenant or one of a small number matters little—nor does it matter if all, some, or no meals are provided. Basically, this is the old rooming house concept, yet it has some merits. In many cases, it is located in the same neighborhood in which your parents lived and in which you grew up. You and your parent may even know the people who own and operate the facility. Living in such a rooming house would cause your mother or father little disruption. He or she could keep the same friends, same doctor, same church, and other familiar contacts, and often some of their same furniture. Provided there is no total alienation or isolation from family members, the system works.

Shared housing, although currently regarded as something new and innovative, is nothing more than a refinement of this same rooming house concept. It involves a large house or apartment occupied by a number of unrelated individuals, usually of the same sex, each having his or her own bedroom furnished with his or her own belongings. The rest of the house—such as the living room, dining room, kitchen, washing machines, etc.—is shared by all residents. The uniqueness of the current concept is in the ownership and operation of such dwellings. Usually this is some nonprofit organization concerned with the care of the elderly. It may even be a health care institution that can provide a wide range of services beyond housing should they be needed. I cannot see any objection to a profit-making corporation being involved in such a venture, provided the homes were operated in a quality manner, but to date I know of none. The owners of these shared facilities usually buy them or receive them through donation. They then renovate them to better accommodate the elderly and look after the maintenance, the selection of residents, and all financial matters including the collection of whatever fees they require. This businesslike operation gives the residents a high degree of stability and security, yet permits them to enjoy an essentially independent lifestyle.

In many cases the home was originally owned by a widow who could not bear to leave the old homestead but yet felt the need for companionship and greater security. If such a shared housing organization were available, she would convey ownership of the property to the charity but would continue to live there with her new friends who were also in need of companionship and security at a price they could afford. I can see this trend expanding. Talk it up in your own community.

There are a number of variations of this concept. One is popularly called the *Share-a-Home program.* It is similar to that mentioned above except that the individual retains ownership and the charitable organization acts primarily as an interviewing and monitoring agency to assist the homeowner in securing and maintaining compatible residents. The advantage, of course, is to the owner and ultimately to his or her heirs. The disadvantage is that it puts the other residents at risk should anything happen to the owner.

If your mother (or father) chooses any of these alternatives, treat her as if she were living in her own home. Actually, that is what it is, but if illness or disability strikes, other arrangements will have to be made. Therefore, keep an ace up your sleeve. Some day you may have to play it!

Living in an Institution

The word *institution* conjures up negative images in most people's minds although this is not necessarily justified. There are still some governmental and even private homes that provide pretty meager room and board to the old and needy, but most of these recipients are without families or from such poor households that they have little opportunity to select their care let alone complain.

However, in recent years society has frowned on such inadequate institutions and has created support programs designed to disperse these individuals into smaller residential facilities scattered throughout the community. This newer type of housing promotes a more homelike atmosphere, but the quality still varies with the level of community support. Fortunately, the aging parents of most of those who read this book will never be involved with these types of custodial facilities.

A more favorable living arrangement is the retirement home or village, although most people avoid the use of the word "institution" in describing this type of housing. These facilities may be organized as either profit-making or nonprofit depending on who owns and operates them. One form provides primarily housing, although other services such as housekeeping, meals, limited shopping, and on-call medical services might be available on a concession basis. You can find this type of residential housing for the elderly in both urban and suburban settings. Rural areas usually do not have the volume of individuals needing such housing to justify such an investment, but the need is also less because of the customary practice of taking care of the elderly within the family setting. In cities these facilities are often converted hotels or older buildings renovated with governmental assistance. In the outlying areas they tend to be new structures, again backed by church or governmental funds. They deviate from the usual commercial rental in that occupancy is restricted to senior or disabled citizens. Because of this, the buildings have been modified to include certain amenities such as emergency call systems, handrails, smoke alarms, increased building security, and public rooms with organized recreational and other programs designed to improve the residents' quality of life.

Another type of retirement housing follows essentially the condominium approach. The buildings' design and architectural planning reflect both the amount of land available and the economic level of the individuals they seek. Primarily, their purpose is to relieve the harried homeowner of the many problems of maintaining a private dwelling.

My favorite form of retirement living for those who are beginning to sense that the upkeep of their own home is getting beyond them is the comprehensive care retirement home or village. Most of these are church- or quasi-church sponsored, but the form of organization impresses me less than the quality of the operation. Most of these places limit their admissions to couples or individuals above some stated age such as fifty-five or sixty. For obvious reasons, they generally accept only those in relatively good health, so if your parents seem like good candidates, speak to them about it early, not when they are already bedridden. Also, remember that many have long waiting lists. Those senior citizens who are lucky enough to gain admission occupy an unfurnished, self-contained apartment for which they pay an entrance or endowment fee not too dissimilar in amount to what it would cost to construct the unit. In addition, they pay a monthly maintenance fee that may vary depending on the number of occupants and the meal plan selected. In reality, most residents sell their homesteads, put down part or all of the resulting proceeds for the entrance fee, and then use the money they save on taxes, utilities, and repairs to help pay the monthly charges. Although refund policies vary, you, as a potential heir, must look at the cost of the unit as money that might not be available to your parents' estate.

It is appropriate to use the word "comprehensive" in describing such facilities, because they provide to their residents just about everything they need except clothing and other personal items. Meal policies differ, but usually there is some flexibility. Many serve three meals a day, some only lunch and dinner, but since every unit has its own kitchenette, the preparation of breakfast is no problem.

Most homes offer a wide variety of recreational and social facilities including lounges, game rooms, craft shops, libraries, swimming pools, beauty shops, and convenience stores. They also provide such activities as church services, movies, bingo, and entertainment presented by outside groups. The greatest benefit to your parents and the most comforting reassurance for you is the availability of on-site medical facilities that include ambulatory care and, if necessary, care in a licensed nursing home. Hospitalization is handled through predetermined transfers. Under such arrangements you will never have to wonder whether your parents are sick and uncared for. That is no small matter, believe me!

Should one of your parents die, the survivor may stay in the original apartment or, in some homes, may move into a smaller unit with lower monthly costs. Many such retirement homes are beginning to build sheltered facilities to accommodate those persons not fully able to take care of themselves yet not needing nursing home care. Is it any wonder, then, why one of my own family members housed in such a retirement home expressed, "Where else could I have lived in my own private home and yet enjoyed these kinds of services and advantages at a moment's notice when I needed them?"

There are a few drawbacks or, at least, alleged drawbacks to such facilities. One is the constant presence of old people. The better homes recognize this and try to inject young people into their programs and get the elderly out to where there is a more normal distribution of age groups. It is also true that residents witness the passing of their friends and neighbors more frequently than if they lived in a typical community. Your own aging parents, regardless of where and with whom they live, are always vividly conscious of their own mortality. Nothing can make it more acute. However, the very closeness of the residents, one to another, builds a comfortable bond between them that is found in few other situations. There is no need in these homes, as there is on the outside, for your parents to wonder which of their small circle of friends would inherit the bottle of fine wine reserved for the last one to survive. In these homes, there is no "last man out," no diminishing circle of friends. As one passes on, another takes his or her place. One never runs out of contemporaries. As in a family, life goes on.

Unfortunately, these comprehensive retirement homes are often quite expensive but probably no more costly than living in a single family home of equal quality if one considers all the factors. It might become your task someday to compare and evaluate these costs, so collect the pertinent data as early as possible. Check out one or two places, and get their rates. Find out if there is a waiting list, and if so, how long it is. Ask yourself if you think it would be a good alternative for your parents. If so, involve them. Most places welcome visitors without obligation. I have toured a number of such facilities, and have seen visitors come away with a far more favorable impression than when they entered.

My hope is that retirement home facilities may be sufficient in number and conveniently spaced so that they could bring families together with the twin advantages that most middle-aged people want for their parents: secure, independent living with as many of the benefits of an extended family as is possible. From my experience the stress associated with the caring for one's aging parents is less to the parents, the adult children, and the grandchildren in comprehensive retirement homes than in any other setting. But again, unless there is constant contact between all members of the family under this arrangement, it is but another form of abandonment. Indeed, a fine facility is no substitute for a caring family.

Wandering About

I am not going to discuss the homeless, the destitute, and the "bag people" who have no place to call home but a park bench. This is a blight on our society for which I have no ready solution.

Rather, I want to mention briefly a breed of elderly whom many of us envy but are too frightened to join. They are happy wanderers who have no fixed home other than a mail drop, who travel the broad land in a motor home or the blue waters in a yacht or sailboat. I have met a few of these senior citizens and have never known a happier or more rational group. They live their golden years as they please. They have reduced their worldly possessions to only those they can carry around. They enjoy a rich circle of friends of the same persuasion whom they meet again and again either by plan or happenstance. If this represents your parents, good for them. Their wanderings may or may not be difficult for you to accept depending on the frequency of communication, but I suggest that you not interfere. Our rising crime rate may offer some deterrent to this unique lifestyle, but I hope not. It would be a shame for this small but deserving segment of society to be denied their freedom and safety.

You must realize that there will come a day when these happy wanderers will no longer be able to wander. Everything we have discussed about the need for the elderly to consider alternative housing arrangements when they are no longer able to handle the burdens of their own home equally applies to the wanderers. Most recognize this themselves and have some plan tucked away for a more conventional future. Nevertheless, it would be reassuring to you if they shared those plans with you, particularly if there were an emergency requiring them to change living arrangements in a hurry. Furthermore, all that has been said about isolation and alienation also applies to this alternative mode of living. Invite them to your immobile home for a spell. Two weeks with you will do them as much good as two weeks on their boat or motor home would do you.

Summary

In many homes you will see plaques, samplers, or other works of art reading "Home Sweet Home." Those three little words summarize this chapter as well as any I could write. Help make your parents' home, wherever it may be, as sweet as it can be. But remember, it can never be that way without the presence of a caring family. That is where you come in!

CHAPTER 7

Lifestyles

I do not wish to deprecate the Golden Rule, which says, "As you wish that men would do to you, do so to them," but when lifestyles are involved, don't use it on your parents. It won't work. We must recognize that lifestyles change with each passing generation. Generally, children do not adopt the lifestyles of their parents, nor do older people pick up the habits of their children. A few old people may let their hair grow and begin to wear beads, and in turn a few young people may adopt the same work ethic and devotion to the homestead as their parents, but these are the exceptions.

Chances are that you and your parents do not share the same idea of what is a good time, and if you foist your attitudes, your values, your habits, and your ideas on them, or they on you, conflict will surely follow. Since you are probably more flexible than they are, conform to your parents' lifestyle as much as possible when you are with them. Do as they do, remembering the old saying, "When in Rome, do as the Romans do." When you return home, out of sight of your parents, you can retreat safely into your own ways of living. A few moments out of character won't kill you, and it may buy family peace.

Careful observers have noted that many parents are disappointed, rebuffed, and uncomfortable when they observe their offspring flaunting or advocating lifestyles with which they do not agree. They worry about what will become of their "baby." They doubt that things will work out for the best, and forget that they did for their own generation and for generations before them. They tend to look at the few tragic exceptions as if they were the rule. Fortunately, few become so worked up as to cut off inheritances, disown their children, or even express their disapproval verbally except in sly passing remarks. But it has been done! Most swallow the indignity silently and wonder where they went wrong. Many parents are not as interested in prying into your lifestyle as they are in not wanting you to condemn the way in which they live or have lived these many years. They recognize that they live differently from you and even more so from your teenager— they just don't want their noses rubbed in it. So if you are spending a weekend with your parents or entertaining them at your place, don't tune the stereo or the TV to punk rock, don't drape your clothes all over the banister and the furniture, watch your speech, and, for heaven's sake, don't suggest you all go to an X-rated movie.

Of course, the problem is compounded if your parents live with you, and you sport long hair and a beard which they despise. Such adornments cannot be taken off and put back on at each encounter as can a pair of ragged jeans. Therefore, at times compromises have to be made by both sides. But at least in most of your relationships, do not do unto them what you would not like done unto you. Keep your lifestyles separate as much as possible.

In spite of this admonition, there are many things about their lives that should concern you and about which you might need to take some initiative. The worst type of lifestyle for elderly people is one of inactivity, yet it is an easy one for them to slide into. If there is no job, no domestic responsibility, and little outside contact forcing them to get up and get going, stagnation will soon set in. Other circumstances may quickly reinforce this inactivity. For example, exercise or even gardening is less appealing if the joints hurt; church and social contacts are hard to maintain without adequate transportation and even harder with poor eyesight or hearing; and outside events are difficult to attend if money is tight. The easy chair in front of the TV becomes a way of life, and their territory shrinks to about the size of a large coffin and serves about the same purpose.

If your parents have succumbed to such a life of inactivity, you may have to light the fuse to blast them out of it. But first try to figure out why they are so inactive. Is it due to deteriorating health? Is it because of lack of funds or transportation? Is it due to an overwhelming depression following the loss of their spouse or closest friend? Is it because of a reluctance to make new friends in a new environment? Each cause has its own remedy, but if your parents have not discovered that remedy by themselves, help them find it. They may only need a little tilt, or they may need such a push that it will demand a sacrifice of both your time and your money. Remember, they got you going when you were young and needed help, so turnabout is fair play.

In most communities there are senior citizen clubs or centers that should meet many of the emotional and activity needs of your parents. The problem is to get them to make the first visit, although they will usually go on their own thereafter. Many individuals who have been homebodies and have never interacted with peer groups find it difficult to break the ice and meet new friends. It is as if they were starting kindergarten a second time, afraid to be left alone with a strange group even of their own age, afraid of possible rejection. Therefore, the trick is to find a way around their fears. Try making the direct suggestion that they give it a whirl, or get somebody to extend an invitation. Do anything to get them to attend. Some old people are harder to bring around than others. I have seen some sit within a group of their contemporaries and stare stonefaced into space, resisting every sign of cordiality. But give them time to work out their emotional difficulties. Don't stop at the first push, because eventually the prodding will work. In small, tightly knit communities where everybody knows everybody else, lifelong animosities may foolishly prevent them from enjoying the company of others who may be as lonely as they are. Maybe it is time for your parents to patch up things with their neighbors. It is rough to go through old age with enemies.

Unfortunately, there are many old people who because of severe illness or disability are unable to leave home without difficulty. If these individuals were in a nursing home, such activities would be brought to them and participation would be geared to their ability by trained staff. Those confined to the home environment deserve the same pleasures, although no one expects you to invite the community singers or the local magician to perform in your parents' bedroom. However, friends and relatives can pop in, and there are cards and games to play, puzzles to work, things to make, books and magazines to read, and television to watch, provided it is not the only escape from their narrowed world and is not the only human voice they hear. Of course, they may feel imposed upon if you try to strike up a conversation during their favorite soap opera, but what is wrong with just holding hands or sipping tea together until the program is over? Some elderly merely need prodding, while others do not know the multitude of diversions that await the curious. Expand their limited world. It can be done. It certainly can be rewarding.

I know that your days and evenings are busy. I know there is much to get done, but why not squeeze in a little time to share with your parents? Try to stimulate neighbors, church groups, and others to do likewise. They just may be waiting for an invitation.

If distance permits, get your children in the habit of visiting their grandparents alone. They will gain a lot from such contacts. Traditions and family history will be kept alive, and stories of what it was like to live a generation ago will be a lesson in history far more impressive than those in school. What is more, they may even learn some manners. But most of all, they will come to realize that caring and loving others of all ages is an important part of life.

If your parents are not deliberately exercising, get them started. Suggest that they consult their physician first to learn whether they *can* exercise—and I bet they can—and to find out how much and what kinds of activities would be best suited to their needs. Walking is one of the best forms of exercise, provided it is done at a brisk and steady pace for at least twenty minutes three or four times a week. Even swimming, bicycling, heavy gardening, or a slow game of tennis are well tolerated by most seniors in reasonably good health. Other activities that do not produce a mild and sustained increase in pulse rate may be entertaining, but generally they are not too helpful in keeping the body in shape. But do not discount anything that keeps the body moving. I am sure my neighbors must think I itch or something because whenever I go out to the box on the street to get the mail or newspapers, I jog, flail my arms, and arch my back. It may look silly, but it gets the kinks out. Incidentally, exercising along with your parents will do more than stir up the juices; it will bring you closer together spiritually as well as physically.

Let me elaborate a bit on gardening, because it fits into the lifestyle of many of today's elderly. It is an activity with many desirable facets. It is not only good exercise, but it can aid nutrition as well as add color and fragrance to the home. It can create an interest and a purpose that last year round in canning, drying flowers, and poring over seed catalogs. It can stimulate social contacts with people of all ages or kindle competition with oneself, one's neighbors, and even at the county fair. It can keep pleasant memories fresh and alive. Many community groups working with the aged recognize the therapeutic effects of gardening. If your parents have the land, urge them to exercise their green thumbs.

Even if your parents are bedridden, exercise is just as essential for them—although their program will differ. If they are under active treatment, their physician should work with a physical therapist to outline an appropriate set of exercises. If and when one of your parents drops down a notch in his or her physical ability, check again with the physician. A new set of less strenuous exercises can be devised. Muscle movement is absolutely necessary for bodily health, particularly for the bedridden or chairbound. It keeps the muscles in tone, exercises the heart, drains the veins—which depend upon muscle action to return the blood to the heart—helps maintain a proper weight, and preserves whatever mobility the individual has left. Mimic the TV exercise programs. Use music to set the tempo as well as to keep the motion going. Share in those exercises if you can. To exercise alone is monotonous; to exercise with someone else is infectious.

The gentle fatigue of exercise is a far better somnifacient than a central nervous system depressant in pill form. Studies have shown that, for the average adult, those who sleep seven or eight hours per night seem to enjoy the best health. Those sleeping nine or more hours appear to be less healthy, and those sleeping six or less hours appear to be the least healthy. But please understand, this is a relationship, not a direct cause and effect. George Burns, the ageless comedian, in responding to a question searching for his secret of longevity, said, "Don't fall in love with your bed." He was right. It is an unhealthy place for an elderly person to spend his or her days unless there is no other choice.

Like house cats, the elderly get some of their sleep in short naps after meals or exercise, while quietly reading or watching TV, or even in midstream conversation. Whenever my father got caught napping under such circumstances, he would always say, "I guess it's the change of air." No, it was not the change of air; it was just the normal thing for someone of his age to do. Recognize it as such. However, if possible, try to help your parents make their days more stimulating and thereby prevent too many naps. As we grow older, our sleep patterns change. Insomnia increases, arousal is easier, and sleep is less intense. It is better for most people to keep intact their twenty-four hour circadian rhythm with its diurnal daylight periods of activity and nighttime periods of rest rather than to fragment sleep into small pieces. As I will mention in Chapter 11, "The Drugs They Take," avoid chronic use of sleeping pills, regardless of age.

Those who stereotype the elderly in movies, plays, and cartoons often focus on their tendency to reminisce and live in a world of memories. Indeed, it is a significant part of the lifestyles of those with long years under their belts. Strange as it may seem, there is considerable professional indecision as to whether reminiscing is valuable or threatening to the individual. One school of thought believes that the repeated recalling of what one did or witnessed in the past is of therapeutic value. These observers believe that reminiscing is a natural process, and that the reliving of events long since past may help resolve hidden internal conflicts that have tarnished the individual's sense of self-worth. They also believe that it may help a person wrap up the loose ends of his or her life and help put his or her house in order in anticipation of death. Of course, to some skeptics this explanation is far too complicated. They believe that the elderly merely find living in the past more pleasant than in the hard realities of the bitter present. For whatever reason, most observers believe that the dredging up of old memories seems to be helpful and, therefore, should be encouraged. As we shall learn later, this phenomenon is referred to as "life review."

On the other hand, another school of thought feels that in those individuals who have led rather uncolorful, unsuccessful, or perhaps unfulfilled lives, the bringing up of their failures and disappointments might lead to despair, depression, and, in extreme cases, suicide.

Nevertheless, both sides seem to agree that those of us who have to listen to their stories should not only tolerate them but also should help the individuals resolve through such recollections any internal conflicts they might have. No life is devoid of value, even if the greatest triumph was bringing you into the world. Something must have been done right! Few can look back and feel that they accomplished everything that they wanted, but also few can look back and feel that they did not accomplish what was reasonably expected of them under the circumstances. By your listening, praising, thanking, and giving dignity to what your parents did accomplish, you can help make their reminiscing a pleasant and effective therapeutic process.

The automobile and your parents grew up together. There was a romance between the two which over the years led to the development of the gas-guzzlers of the late seventies. It was a heady period, and your parents have not forgotten it. They still like to drive. In fact, for many elderly individuals the car has become a necessity. Therefore, it is little wonder that when that freedom of mobility is denied, they feel that their world has collapsed into a black hole. Most of the elderly will not give up driving on their own initiative. Rather it takes an accident, blindness, a stroke, mental illness, or the revocation of their license to bring it to a halt. Fred Astaire, then in his eighties, once revealed on a talk show that as he drove around Hollywood, people shouted insults at him because he drove so slowly and cautiously. Apparently he held up traffic for all it was worth. But that didn't faze him. He kept right on driving, and I have known many others, some into their nineties, to do the same. We have all been behind that kind of driver as we tried to rush to an appointment we thought was important. But bully for them! They may not be flashy, but they are reasonably safe. More importantly, they are happy and independent.

The American Association of Retired Persons recognizes the paradox between the desire to drive and the competency to drive. Consequently, the AARP has developed a Driver Improvement Program which it presents in various cities around the country. These seminars last two and a half days and are designed to help the elderly improve their driving practices.

Nevertheless, many middle-aged individuals will be faced with a problem concerning the family car. They will see their parents' driving skills deteriorate. Minor scratches and dents will appear on the car and on the garage doors without adequate explanation. Insurance rates will begin to climb. Restrictions may be imposed on their driving by licensing authorities. What should you do? Certainly you worry not only about your parents' safety, but also about the lives and property of others. Whose responsibility is it? It may be the state's, but your peace of mind, to say nothing of your inheritance, may also be on the line. Yet you have no authority to ground your parents.

Before turning your back on the situation of trying to take some sort of action, collect the facts. Have your parents already put some limitations on their own driving? Many do. They may first cut out night driving, then give up long-distance driving, and, finally, avoid rush hour traffic. You will know if your parents have placed some restrictions on themselves. They will drive only between midmorning and midafternoon and then only for shopping, appointments with the doctor, and other short trips of necessity—no long joy rides. This will be their pattern until they either receive a police citation or suffer some deteriorating health problem—whichever comes first. Count yourself lucky if they stop before they do any bodily harm to themselves or others.

Losing one's ability to drive is a devastating blow to the individuals who unrealistically sees him- or herself as someone still able to handle a vehicle. It is a shock, a serious loss of independence; it is a closed door through which they will never again pass; it is a loud and clear signal that the end of their own road is not too far off. However, you can do very little about this sad situation.

One thing you should not do is to sell the car; that is too much stripping away too soon. With the car in the garage there is hope—not much, but hope. Its very presence will bring memories of its purchase, of the places it has taken your parents, and of the pleasure it has given. There will be plenty of time to dispose of it. Let your parents decide its disposition—after all, it is theirs. They may even enjoy giving it to some favorite friend or relative, permitting them to receive warm words of appreciation at a time when they are still able to hear them.

I doubt if their present car will stir up as many backseat romantic memories as did the beatup jalopy they bought in their virile youth, but do not think that the years have erased all thoughts of physical passion. Most middle-aged persons find it difficult to imagine their aging parents participating in active physical lovemaking, and some even find it disgusting. What hypocrites! Where does it say that sexual activity has an age limit? Most researchers in human sexuality state that, except in cases where extreme health problems prohibit it, the urge for sexual expression continues. It may change in frequency and intensity but not in desire or enjoyment. There is more hand-holding, more touching and caressing, more of the softer and gentler expressions of love, but it is every bit as meaningful and pleasurable. Recently I have noticed a number of TV films about the elderly portraying this kind of affection. It is good education for all of us.

Much of society fails to understand this fact of life. Until recently most nursing homes would not let a man and wife share a double room. Many hospitals still do not. Apparently they believe that it is against God's will, the public interest, or something equally unsubstantiated to permit any sexual affinity in old age.

The next time you are at church, on a bus, or at a public gathering, look at an elderly couple, or at an elderly single for that matter, and ask yourself why they should not enjoy sexual relations as much as you do. If you feel they should not, if you snicker, or if you feel there is something perverted about the whole subject, you are in trouble with your aging parents. Even if you never discuss the subject—certainly your parents won't—your feelings will show through and conflicts will develop.

Many of these biological urges that motivated your parents to marry and eventually to bring you into the world continue even after the loss of a spouse. If these urges become strong enough and are coupled with the need for companionship, they may precipitate a second marriage. For reasons difficult to understand, many middle-aged people often disapprove of such marriages. Their loving father suddenly becomes a dirty old man; a lonely mother becomes a gold-digger. But as Henri Rousseau, the late nineteenth-century French primitive painter, then sixty-five, wrote, "It's at my age that one most needs one's heart warmed up again. It is not right to laugh at old people who get married again; you need the company of someone you love." Try to treat this facet of your parents' lives with maturity. You do not need to know any intimate details, but please, do not show any signs of surprise or disapproval. They certainly will not try to control your sex life anymore, so who are you to try to control theirs?

Most of us do not associate divorce with old age, yet it occurs. The cause is probably not infidelity or sexual incompatibility, but rather, it is more likely due to some long-festering frustration sparked by the realization that life is coming to an end. Before it does, there is a yearning for one last taste of happiness. The action may be unsound, intemperate, even irrational, but it bursts forth with great passion. The distraught individual will let go with some remark such as, "I can't stand his (or her) harping any longer. I'm fed up! I'm leaving!" Can you sense this pent-up ill feeling early enough to prevent such an explosive outburst? If you live close to your parents, I think you can. Obviously, the remedy is bilateral: lower one partner's tendency to irritate and raise the other's tolerance of it. This is no easy job considering you are not dealing with particularly flexible people. Professional counseling could help, but, even though the odds of getting your parents to go that route without an awful lot of insight seems remote, it is still worth the try. What if you are left with the problem? Try to decompress the situation the best way you can. Persuade your parents to distrust the old but unreliable saying, "The grass is greener on the other side of the fence." In fact the legal snarls can brown the grass on both sides and can tarnish the glitter of any such impulsive thought. Another helpful trick is to spend more time with them. Parents tend to behave better in front of their offspring. Consequently, the opportunity to be unloving to each other may be sufficiently reduced to restore some degree of compatibility.

By now you should know enough about your parents to react to their own lifestyle with grace and understanding. The Golden Rule applies in many broad facets of human intercourse: honesty, integrity, and devotion. But it does not apply in the lesser ways of life. You must learn to understand and accept that your mores and those of your parents will differ. Bolster theirs but do not force yours upon them. Many of the conflicts between the middle-aged and their parents swirl around differing lifestyles. Remember, you are the more flexible of the two unless your parents brought you up wrong. Use that flexibility and practice your understanding. It is a big part of caring for your aging parents.

As a parent, it is your job to be concerned about the lifestyle of your children. But it is not your job to act like a parent with your own parents. You have to act differently: concerned, yes; involved, yes; loving, yes; but totally responsible, no.

CHAPTER 8

Keep 'Em
Busy

Photo courtesy of Milwaukee Sentinel

*I*n 1775 Immanuel Kant, the German philosopher, wrote, "The busier we are, the more acutely we feel that we live, the more conscious we are of life." If your aging parents have not yet learned that 200-year-old lesson, scribble it on a small piece of paper and tape it to their bathroom mirror. They'll get the message!

If keeping busy were just a matter of fun and games, I would not pay much attention to it. That is not my field—preventive medicine is. But since there is a direct relationship between health and inactivity in the post-retirement years, I am not only interested, I am concerned. I purposely make the distinction between the pre-retirement and the post-retirement years because of the tremendous effect that retirement can have upon the lives of both your father and mother. With retirement can come boredom, loss of self-image, and lack of purpose. Your father may feel lost, washed up. Your mother will not only sense your father's distress, but she will also suffer her own. She may feel that all she was born to accomplish has been accomplished; nothing more is left. Both are candidates for depression and a wide range of psychosomatic illnesses. Putting purpose back into their lives will help erase these dangers. While it will not guarantee immortality, it could well increase their longevity and reduce their morbidity (the incidence of illness). I recently read about a gentleman nearing his 100th birthday who was given an outdoor lounge chair as a present. However, he would not use it in his yard for fear the neighbors might think him lazy. Although he was an exception, it does suggest that there is some merit in keeping busy.

The possibilities for doing this are endless. In fact, most retirees are involved with a number of favorite activities. Certainly, there should be no excuse for a senior citizen to act like some whining preschooler asking his mother, "What can I do today?" If your parents were self-starters when they were young, they will probably keep themselves busy in their golden years without your help. Lucky for you! You will have one less thing to worry about. However, if they lived dull, humdrum lives when they were young—whether by choice or by necessity—they will tend to stay that way. But now there is every reason for them to discontinue that destructive pattern; the confining boredom which earning a living or raising a family may have imposed upon them is over. A new day is dawning, and some important changes are in order. So watch your parents. They may be in need of some prompting to get the maximum out of their post-retirement years.

Obviously, age and state of health significantly influence the activities your parents may enjoy. It is conceivable that as the years pass, your mother or father might take on and then have to give up a number of different avocations. My father-in-law, after retiring from a distinguished career in architecture, took up wood carving. He spent long hours creating beautiful family treasures, but as age and illness crept up on him, the blocks of wood became too heavy and the chiseling and polishing too strenuous, so he shifted to oil painting. From then on he continued to produce a whole new category of masterpieces. The point is that he kept busy at whatever was appropriate at the time. Your parents may have different interests, but they too may have to shift to less strenuous pursuits as the years pass. Churchill, Eisenhower, and thousands of others have, so why not your parents?

I should like to suggest seven broad categories of activities that you might offer your parents should they ever ask, "What can I do today?" They are:

1. Continue to work
2. Volunteer
3. Engage in politics
4. Get more education
5. Enjoy recreational activities
6. Pursue a hobby or craft
7. Keep in touch with family and friends

Continue to Work

Work is the most satisfying activity for that mass of today's elderly who were brought up with a strong work ethic. Now that we have more flexible age limits for retirement, many workers will be able to continue quite happily in their jobs for years longer than ever before. This is what many of the elderly want, although in time they too will have to look over the same list of post-retirement options as did their predecessors.

An even better alternative is to shorten the workweek gradually. Like breaking any other habit, it is often easier to taper off than to stop cold turkey. Unfortunately, this opportunity is not available to everyone. I have always had the hunch that more workers could follow this route if only they were willing to talk it over with their bosses and were willing to be flexible in their hours and duties. I would also hope that, where necessary, unions might permit such a stretched-out time and pay schedule. It would be in the interest of their members if they did. As I indicated in Chapter 4, I have recently noted that a number of firms are beginning to use their retired workers as substitutes for those employees who are ill or on vacation. That is a great idea serving both the company and the retirees admirably. If your father and mother have not suggested these two desirable alternatives to their superiors and have not made known their availability, have them give it a whirl.

Serving as a part-time consultant is another excellent way to stay in touch, feel wanted, and contribute to the cause. Unfortunately, this opportunity is open to only a very few individuals and generally not for as long as might be helpful. But it can serve as an excellent transitional option. However, in due time another choice of activity will have to be selected, but by that time the individual may understand his or her own physical and emotional needs enough to make an intelligent decision.

Whenever a person can no longer continue in his or her original line of work, it does not mean that he or she can no longer work. It only means that they have to change jobs or take on something new. It does not mean that a machine operator or a private secretary has to learn some outlandish new skill, but if a person is physically fit and flexible in attitude, there are many part-time, even full-time jobs for the asking that younger workers refuse. Unfortunately, they may be less prestigious and offer less pay or less convenient hours, but what is the goal? It is to keep busy, and since it is work, not play, to earn a little money as well. Actually, a change to a less demanding job can be quite stimulating and satisfying. Don't let your parents knock it. It is better than moping around the house all day.

Of course, once your parents start receiving Social Security retirement payments, the government will withhold $1 in benefits for each $2 of earned income above certain limits set yearly by Congress. Although the amount changes yearly, Social Security will advise your parents of the current allowable amounts in an envelope stuffer early in each calendar year. Incidentally, your working parent or parents will also have to pay Social Security tax as well as income tax on their earnings just as if they were not retired. This reduces the economic value of working, but the benefits to one's psyche and well-being remain high.

If the trend toward early retirement continues for those with a less compulsive work ethic, the need to keep busy will extend over a much longer period and may require even more careful planning to assure a happy and healthy post-retirement lifestyle.

The one special activity I always like to advocate is writing. On some occasions it might be considered work for pay and at other times work without pay depending upon the individual's skill and luck. It can be poetry or prose, a book, a play, a short story, or a newspaper article. It can be a genealogy, a family history, children's story, or any other kind of original writing. Perhaps the best way to explain this possibility is by extracting pieces from an article I wrote for a small publication entitled "How to Write and Sell," prepared by a group of working authors who call themselves the Raconteurs.

Excerpts from *Writing in Retirement*

There are many satisfying alternatives to retirement. One is called retooling—learning a new skill like painting, woodworking, even playing golf or fishing, but the most satisfying of them all . . . is writing. . . . Writing opens up a whole new career, one which completely befits the senior citizen. Although it takes discipline, it is not pervasively confining. Under most circumstances it can be measured to match your own needs and responsibilities. If you want to visit the grandchildren, take a brief vacation or just work around the house, do it. You have no deadlines to meet, no boss to ask. . . . Early in life you should have learned to listen and to observe the world around you. . . . If among those memories or events . . . you find something of interest, chances are someone else will find it of equal interest, but unless you convey that observation either by word of mouth or by the written page, no one else will ever share in its pleasure. . . . Although a writer must distinguish the interesting from the mundane, a great event is not necessarily interesting, nor a sunset necessarily mundane. It is what the author makes of it that is the difference. . . . Nor can a writer forget about people, the people who may well become the characters about whom he will write . . . but unless you observe them, remember them and get to understand them, they will be lost to history. . . . Much of our reward and joy of writing must be in keeping our memories alive, our brains active and in great measure in the act of writing itself.

If your parents are the writing kind, tease them with these few words—like a vaccination, it might take.

Although I have written for professional publications for many years, it was not until I passed sixty-five that I joined three writing groups. Here I met many new, wonderful friends. To my surprise, few were professionally trained. Many were housewives, widows, or retirees who had led interesting lives, had many memories worth preserving, and were willing to invest time to improve their writing skills. They are happy, busy people! Your parents might like being one of them. Do not let their unliterary backgrounds inhibit them. In every crowd there is an unpolished diamond waiting for its brilliance to be revealed.

Work is not a dirty, four-letter word, even in retirement. To many it is a salvation; to others it is a bonus. To no one is it a disservice. It all depends on one's needs and interests. A world without work would be a pretty dull place. All that should matter to your aging parents is the quality and quantity of the work itself and the amount of joy and satisfaction they receive from it.

Volunteer

If the volunteer movement had not been created to fill the unmet needs of many of this country's nonprofit institutions and organizations, it would have had to be invented as a healthy outlet for senior citizens. It has become the number one activity open to individuals who have time to spare and who sense the need to be useful to themselves as well as to others. While volunteering started out as a charitable act with great potential for self-enrichment and personal growth, it has recently become a part of national policy. Our government is looking to volunteerism to help maintain our coveted way of life without resorting to ever-increasing taxes. Therefore, it has taken on the added aura of a community responsibility.

If your mother has been active in volunteer work in some organization for many years, urge her to continue. But how about your father? Many men have begun to volunteer, but many more are needed. Now is your chance to get him out of the house into something new and challenging. He might be surprised at the many men just like himself who are already busy and happy giving of their time and of themselves.

The organizations which at this moment are down on their knees praying for more volunteers are legion. There should be one to match the interest of every person wanting something to do. A partial list includes:

- Hospitals
- Libraries
- Churches
- Schools
- Museums
- Nature centers
- Historical sites
- Youth organizations
- Day care centers
- Governmental programs

Many local newspapers carry periodic notices of organizations looking for volunteers. If your parents have not thought of the possibility of offering this type of helping hand, plant the seed. It will be good for them, good for the organization they work for, and good for the country.

In addition to the obvious value of volunteering to both the individual and the agency, there are a number of incidental benefits that should not be overlooked. Your parents will have the opportunity to make new friends, young and old, who share the same interests. I have seen widows and widowers meet other lonely individuals whereupon nature has taken its course. Most organizations with a large corps of volunteers show their appreciation by arranging special programs, banquets, and awards ceremonies, and some even offer special purchasing and other privileges. But most importantly, they offer a sense of belonging to something substantial. Every human being including your parents needs some warm bond of allegiance. Finally, if and when they ever find themselves on the receiving end of someone else's volunteer services, they will be less embarrassed, more appreciative, and better able to accept such care. That's no small consideration.

At first blush most of us do not think of government as being a worthy place to give freely of our time and talents, particularly if we have given the IRS so much without benefit of volunteering. Nevertheless, there is a rather wide variety of governmental programs that depend on volunteers for success.

The Service Corps of Retired Executives (SCORE), sponsored by the federal Small Business Administration, offers the opportunity for skilled individuals to provide management counseling and training to owners and operators of small businesses and to people who are considering starting a small business. What a splendid way for your father or mother to help a neighbor and at the same time to savor vicariously the success of a new business.

For those who are sharp at figures and feel challenged by the IRS, there are two programs officially recognized by the U.S. Treasury Department. One is Voluntary Income Tax Assistance (VITA); the other is Tax Counseling for the Elderly (TCE). The first group assists the low-income, handicapped, and non-English speaking individuals in completing the various 1040 forms, while the second group does the same for the elderly. Friends of mine who have served as volunteers in those programs report that they have received a great deal of personal satisfaction from their participation. By learning more about their less fortunate fellow citizens, they also have become more tolerant and sensitive human beings.

The federal government also funds an agency entitled ACTION which in turn makes financial grants on a project basis through three volunteer programs. The first is the Retired Senior Volunteer Program (RSVP). In 1981 it spent over $26 million for 707 projects in all 50 states, the District of Columbia, the Virgin Islands, and Guam involving more than 26,000 volunteers over 60 years of age. Since the projects are designed to meet the needs of local communities, the variety of services offered run from A (domestic abuse) to Z (helping zoos) and absolutely everything in between. Your parents can get more information by contacting ACTION, which is listed in most phone books under "U.S. Government" or by calling their local Office of Aging.

The second activity is the Foster Grandparents Program, which is available to elderly men and women of low income who work for four hours, five days a week with children who have special physical, educational, or emotional needs. Although considered a volunteer program, the participants are currently given a small hourly stipend.

The last of the three ventures, the Senior Companion Program, uses the same format as the Foster Grandparents, only it directs its efforts toward helping other senior citizens to remain in their own homes. Actually, your parents might fit into this program either as a volunteer or as a beneficiary should they need help themselves.

Local governments have other projects in which volunteers are welcomed. A call to any county or municipal office should steer your aging parents to one of these programs.

Consequently, if your parents have time on their hands, have a need to feel wanted, and are compassionate to the less fortunate, but for some reason have not thought of the possibility of volunteering in some community institution or agency, suggest it to them. It has worked wonders for others, and your parents should be no exception.

I would be remiss if I did not include in this section the "job jar," which in every household cries out for some free help. Although it may seem more like the Army's version of volunteering, it is work around the house which needs to be done and for which there is little direct reimbursement. Nevertheless, your father can be kept pleasantly busy by trying to empty the jar, but remember, like a cool spring feeding a tiny stream, it can never be permanently emptied.

Engage in Politics

Whereas some of the previous suggestions illustrated how your aging parents might volunteer their services to certain governmental programs, they were nonpartisan. What I am suggesting now is strictly political, strictly partisan. Running for public office could be a towering cap to anyone's career, man or woman's. Senior citizens have held every political office from President of the United States on down and at every level of government: federal, state, county, and municipal. There is no good reason why your parents should not be in that august company. Many of these positions do not require great political experience—most merely take courage, common sense, and commitment plus enough votes to make it happen. Gray power is a political reality that can be exploited to put other senior citizens into office. It might just be to your parents' liking.

Even if they do not run for elective office, there are still appointive positions open at every level of government. In fact, there are more of these jobs available than elected posts. Many may match your parents' experience: the town planning board for the builder or engineer, the recreation board for the teacher or housewife. Democracy demands able people with sufficient time to give to their community. Although I do not think that government should be run entirely by graybeards, certainly older people should be proportionately represented. Most senior citizens who hold such office, provided they are of sound mind and flexible spirit, do well in government. They are more likely to have their eyes on the public interest than on the next election. That makes them more statesmen and stateswomen than politicians. Even if your parents are not interested in direct political participation, suggest to them that they urge their local senior citizens' club to search out some likely candidate for some local office. Many local positions are not strictly partisan. Candidates can be independent, representing a community-wide platform. It is from such little political acorns that mighty leaders grow.

Even if your parents shun both elective and appointive office, they may still be willing to work for a candidate. They certainly would be welcomed with open arms because no politician can be successful without a corps of loyal and enthusiastic campaign workers. These jobs are usually suitable to senior citizens: distributing materials, telephoning, and dozens of other tasks requiring few special skills and little physical exertion. Give your parents a cause that can keep 'em busy.

Get More Education

Photographs of senior citizens in graduation caps and gowns make great grist for every newspaper editor. We see such pictures every year with predictable regularity. But your parents do not have to go that far. There are many in-between stops, but remember, learning is one of the best ways to keep an older person emotionally and, to a certain extent, physically healthy. It provides a purpose in life, permits accomplishment, requires discipline of mind and body, widens the intellectual horizon, stimulates new friendship, and prepares the individual for years of pleasurable activity. Education creates a new or improved self-image. Students have something to talk about, something to show off.

Would more education benefit either of your parents? Studying and learning can occur at any level—from home study to graduate school. For some, the stimulus might be the completion of some academic degree cut short years ago for all sorts of reasons. This unplanned interruption may not gnaw at them during their busy earning years, but it can begin to eat away during retirement. Perhaps now is the time to get that diploma.

On the other hand, they may be satisfied to learn something new at home, on their own initiative. During their long lifetimes, many elderly people have had an experience which during retirement teases them into knowing more about that subject. Perhaps they have traveled to a country about which they want to learn more. The library can be their resource. Other pursuits may require not only self-instruction but also some equipment to get started. For example, they may have seen samples of fine handiwork: sewing, woodcarving, painting, ceramics, and other skills. Now they find that they would like to try their own hand at one of them. Fine, the opportunity is there.

Many colleges and universities will allow senior citizens to audit courses at a very small fee, permitting students like your parents to attend classes but avoid examinations and, of course, degree credits. In addition, many of them participate in the programs operated by Elderhostel, Inc., an international nonprofit corporation whose goal is "to serve older adults by offering them educational programs at modest costs." These are on-campus experiences of about one week duration geared to the senior citizen. If your parents are not already on their mailing list, write the Elderhostel people at 100 Boylston Street, Boston, MA 02116. You and your parents will be amazed at the variety of excellent offerings. The community colleges and local technical schools are also very helpful in providing a wide variety of special programs for the elderly.

I hope your parents are looking into such educational possibilities. If they have not thought of further education or have toyed with the idea but never got around to it, here is your chance. Give them a push. If they do not know where to turn for information, have them consult their local Office on Aging. But by hook or crook get your parents back into school. They will probably like it the second time around better than they did the first. This time it will be fun, not drudgery. As the cereal commercial suggests, "It will be good for them."

Enjoy Recreational Activities

We now see older people jogging, biking, swimming, and playing tennis, whereas some years ago it was strictly shuffleboard and miniature golf. Yet many who should be out jumping around continue to sit still. The problem is, how do you get them started? You might want to give them a membership in a fitness center or buy them some sporting togs or equipment as birthday gifts. That may give them the necessary hint. Invite them to go along with you when you exercise. Bring up the subject when they are firmly ensconced in their recliners in front of the TV. The contrast should be sufficient.

Of course, not all recreation is physical. Many people indulge in spectator sports, which provide an interest, an outlet, probably some companionship, and even a modicum of exercise, parking lots being located where they are around most stadiums. So how about a couple of ducats to some event? That will get them out of the house. It may even start a habit.

As disability or just plain frailty catches up with older people, there is a tendency to reduce activity to almost nothing. Going to the bathroom becomes the longest walk of the day. For shame! How about getting them to walk around the block or the neighborhood? As I mentioned under lifestyles, if they have a yard, keep them puttering around in it. Keep them planting flowers, weeding, trimming the bushes, anything to keep them busy and physically active. If circumstances prevent them from going outside as it might in inclement weather, get them into some form of indoor exercises or calisthenics. Regular exercise for perhaps twenty minutes a day either before breakfast or mid-morning will do them worlds of good. It should be vigorous enough to quicken their pulse and stir up their juices, providing, of course, that they have their doctor's permission. Again, the question is, "What gifts might stimulate some of this indoor activity?" Although special equipment is not a necessity, the fact that most of it is too bulky to hide serves as a constant reminder to exercise. Therefore, you might consider an indoor exercise bicycle, a carpet putting gadget, an over-the-door shoulder exerciser, or any of a dozen or more pieces of indoor physical fitness equipment found in any sporting goods or department store. Next to pushing away from the dining room table, it will be the best form of exercise they can get. Remember, the sooner your parents settle down into their comfortable easy chairs, the sooner they will lose their mobility and the sooner you will end up as the caregiver to an aging and handicapped parent. Try to avoid that as long as possible.

Games and athletics are not for everyone. For some, recreation comes in more cultural pursuits: travel, music, theater, and the other arts. All of these activities provide the same opportunity for learning, keeping busy, getting out of the house, meeting other people, and even various amounts of walking. I don't even care if some just saunter down to the local tavern as long as they go light on the drinking and heavy on the fellowship and checkers. If that has been your father's practice in his earlier years, don't try to reform him. Just see that he is kept busy doing what he enjoys as long as he gets some exercise going back and forth.

Of course, if your parents are farmers or if they pursue some other active lifestyle, you will have little trouble getting them to exercise whether sick or well. Your problem may be just the opposite. You may want them to work less and enjoy recreation more.

Pursue a Hobby or Craft

I've often been asked, "What are your hobbies?" To this date I have never come up with a good answer. I never got into collecting coins or stamps, never hooked rugs, made bird houses, played golf or raised guppies. I have kept the house, yard, and car in reasonable shape, but no one labels them hobbies. Nor did I ever have much of a passion to start something new when I retired. I still don't. I just seem to continue what I have always done—teach, read, write, and consult in matters of health affairs. But now I do it more leisurely. So far I have not felt the urge to buy a hobby kit or to fill my basement with craft supplies. Perhaps when I can no longer pursue my present activities I might have to reconsider.

However, there are those who are totally lost once they retire. Perhaps they have moved to smaller quarters, making it even harder to choose an enjoyable hobby or craft. Yet I have seen any number of older people living in apartments or retirement villages who have fixed up corners of their bedrooms as hobby centers. Those people have something to get up for in the morning. They exercise their minds, and, if not their entire bodies, at least enough joints to stay nimble.

It is difficult, even an affront, to try to force your parents into a hobby of your choosing. They may not be attuned to the same things that would interest you. One advantage of a retirement village or home is the presence of a hobby and craft shop often well equipped for a wide variety of activities. Hobbies are generally contagious, one picking up an interest from someone else. Often the equipment itself stimulates the choice. For example, the real fun of photography is not just the picture-taking but the ability to develop, print, and display the shots. Most private homes do not have a well-equipped darkroom, but many retirement homes do. This can give the impetus to an otherwise dormant or frustrated hobby.

Cooking and keeping house, although not glamorous, can give your parents something to do. These activities require time, skill, and experience in order to do them well. However, when these are removed, as they might be if your parents enter a retirement home where meals and housekeeping services are provided, they will need to find some other ways to fill this time. (Incidentally, cooking is as good a hobby for men as it is for women.)

If your folks could develop a hobby or craft requiring or adaptable to group participation, so much the better. Often a team effort is more satisfactory than a solitary hobby. Occasionally a hobby might augment an individual's income or lead to gifts benefiting some charity.

A request from you to your parents may stimulate a hobby. Suggest that their granddaughter might like a dollhouse or a grandson might need some help with a model train layout. Then watch the fingers fly. You may be able to get your parents out of any destructive and debilitating rut they have fallen into.

Should time drag for your parents or should they become moody because they see nothing left in life but waiting, fill those voids with a hobby. Don't let boredom get them down. Don't let them feel sorry for themselves. Don't let them live their lives without some form of physical and mental activity. Without question, hobbies and crafts are excellent ways of keeping them busy. Your job is to help them find that perfect activity if they do not have enough spunk to find it for themselves.

Keep in Touch with Family and Friends

Older people are and should be the family chroniclers. It is a role which, like writing, befits the senior citizen. A family separated by time and distance is surprisingly fragile, and to stay strong it needs the glue of communication that only a family chronicler can provide. Letters to relatives and friends are valuable, but the most precious gift your parents could offer is a family genealogy augmented by a family history, complete with the accomplishments and tragedies of past and present family members. This should be written down and documented with pictures and whatever records are available. A family health history should be attached to this compendium, as it may come in handy when you least expect it.

Perhaps this business of family roots sounds dull to you, but mark my word, once the information is lost, it is gone forever. A shoebox filled with unmarked photos, letters, and mementos is nothing but junk, but an organized family history is a treasure. Therefore, if your parents do not offer to take on this task, draft them. It will add meaning to their lives, provide intellectual stimulation, and offer a feeling of self-worth that no other endeavor can match. You would be surprised at how many older people are working on such projects.

As your parents age, their circle of friends will tend to melt away. If either they or their friends move to some distant city, the process will be accelerated. Do not let them become isolated. Ask about their friends and suggest they visit or invite them for a visit. Encourage new acquaintances to keep their circle of friends expanding. They need them. You need them because the more friends they have, the less dependent they will be on you. I do not say this in any disparaging way, or as a method of lessening your responsibility. Quite to the contrary, it is a way to keep them interested, happy, and outgoing. When the circle gets tight, there is little to do. Dependency can come only too easily. It will not be long before you will hear them say, "I have nothing to do." Don't let that happen. A wide circle of friends strengthened by a close-knit family will prevent dependency and loneliness to a great extent. Nothing could be finer than being busy with one's own family and friends.

Summary

We have reviewed seven broad ways of keeping your parents busy. Although your role is neither that of a cruise director nor a recreational therapist, it is that of someone whose aging parents are susceptible to many emotional and physical ailments caused by inactivity. Most parents do not need the stimulation of their children to keep them busy at this time in their lives but, unfortunately, many do. Unless you are observant and make certain direct inquiries, you may miss the opportunity to apply a little preventive medicine to your parents' old age. They will be happier and healthier if you do. What is more, they will be less of a burden to you than they might otherwise be. Yes, keeping them busy is one of the best ways of caring for your aging parents.

Getting Around

Ｏne of the distinguishing characteristics of animals—and we are animals—is the power of locomotion, the ability to get around. Your parents may have been fortunate enough to have retained their mobility. On the other hand, they may be bedridden or confined to a very restricted space. Between these two extremes are many gradations of mobility. Therefore, it would seem best if I divided this subject into five levels: getting around one's room, one's home, one's community, one's nation, and finally one's access to the whole world and beyond. As expected, I am going to limit my remarks to those matters which primarily concern the caring of your aging parents. I am not going to discuss the dozens of other peripheral factors of getting around.

Getting Around One's Room

The ultimate tragedy in life, particularly to those who have been active, is the sudden loss of the ability to move about. I am not referring to temporary conditions such as a sore back, a broken leg, or an open wound. I am talking about paralyses: quadriplegia (the paralysis of all four limbs), paraplegia (the paralysis of the lower half of the body or of the legs), and hemiplegia (the paralysis of one side of the body). For those who suddenly experience such immobility following an accident or a stroke, for example, it is a devastating physical and mental shock. The addition of complications such as the loss or jumbling of speech or the presence of mental confusion only compounds the problem for you and for them. Fortunately, in most cases the patient is hospitalized so that both medical and psychological help is readily available.

Should this tragedy befall one of your parents, your role will be very clear, to give immediate support not only to whichever parent suffered the disability but also to the one who did not. These are times of great crisis affecting all members of the family. The patient, depending on the depth of his or her inner strength, may face this problem with amazing hope and optimism or with complete dejection accompanied by thoughts of self-destruction. The goal, of course, is to help sustain hope in the hopeful and to induce hope in the hopeless. It is not a time for hand-wringing or any kind of Pollyanna talk. It is a time for a stiff upper lip and a show of every kind of strength and grit within your body and soul.

Actually there is some justification for such an optimistic approach. Following many spinal cord injuries and most strokes, unless

they are overwhelming, there is some improvement. Whatever disability you see the first day is not likely to be what you will see a
month later. The attending physician will tell you how severe the
damage has been and what he or she predicts for the future. That
should give you some guidance as to what to do and say to your father
or mother during the early days of his or her immobility.

With the geographical distribution of the population in this
country, there is a chance that your parent, if stricken, would be taken
to a small hospital which, although of high quality, might be limited
in its ability to provide rehabilitation services. Do not be embarrassed
to ask the attending physician whether the institution has adequate
facilities for proper rehabilitation. It is your right to know, and it is
your parents' future that is at stake. If it does not, request that your
mother or father be transferred as soon as it is medically possible—not
weeks later—to an institution that offers such care. This may be inconvenient if it is not located in your local community but think of
the needed care he or she will receive, not of your own personal disruption. Paralyses may lead to many serious complications: contrac-
tions, decubitus ulcers, circulatory, urinary or intestinal problems, and
so on. Some of these complications can be prevented by good nursing
care in any hospital, but others can best be handled in a special
rehabilitative unit staffed by trained therapists and equipped with
many innovative devices designed to help maximize whatever mobility the patient has left.

Although I have stressed paralyses as a major cause of immobility, there are many other serious illnesses which are so debilitating as
to render a person immobile. In those situations your response should
be much the same as with paralysis but with one significant exception.
Whereas the patient suffering from an accident may have to live with
his or her disability over many years and the victims of stroke or neurological disease a reasonable length of time, the individual made immobile by heart disease, cancer, or similar illness may be faced with a
more terminal prospect.

It is in these latter situations where friends and relatives find the
most difficulty, and accordingly, many respond in an inappropriate
manner. As a society, we do not handle impending death well. It
scares us. It makes us uncomfortable. Therefore, we tend to avoid it.
Most of us do not know what to do or to say when visiting a dying
patient, so we tend to sweep the problem away by mouthing irrational
hopes of cures and happy times together in the future when we know
there will be none. I do not want to deprive anyone of hoping for mir-

acles. They do occur, but they must be based upon some statistically reliable ray of hope. In many cases there is no such hope, and it is in these cases where we fail our parents the most.

But at the moment let us be optimistic and assume that after a time in the hospital your parent will be able to go home. I will discuss later how to handle the problems of those who for many reasons will have to be placed in facilities other than their own homes as well as those who succumb to an accident or illness. If your parent's problem stems from an accident, his or her degree of disability, once stabilized, will probably not materially change over the years. The goal of his or her future care will be to preserve what powers are left. On the other hand, those who suffered strokes might reasonably expect some improvement with good physical therapy. In either case, you will have to prepare your home for his or her homecoming. Your parent's limited world will change from an institutional focus to a domestic one. Actually, it will be something in between. It will have some of the appearances of a normal bedroom, but it will also contain many of the same pieces of medical equipment with which your father or mother became familiar during his or her hospitalization: a hospital-type bed, a bedside commode, a trapeze for pulling oneself up, or an over-the-bed table. Whatever it does contain will be your parent's habitat for an indefinite period.

How do you go about fixing such a room? Certainly it cannot be completely converted to a fun-filled environment, but your job will be to put as much imagination into it as possible. In Chapter 17, "Three Ways to Cope," I will discuss in considerable detail how your parent's room might be physically arranged, regardless of whether it will be used primarily as a bedroom or as a sickroom. But at this point we are dealing with an aging parent who is returning home from a spell of unwelcomed hospitalization. Depending upon the anticipated length of immobility you might wish to pick and choose from Chapter 17 those suggestions that would seem most appropriate in your particular set of circumstances.

After you have arranged the room, you will have to consider the essential pieces of patient-care equipment you will need to make the room acceptable for your parent's homecoming. His or her physician, physical therapist, or social worker should be able to help you obtain these necessary items. In most communities there are a number of procurement sources. They can be rented from a sickroom supply house, purchased from a drugstore, or borrowed from a loan closet which some hospitals, churches or social agencies operate for just such a purpose. Some can even be made at home with a little ingenuity. Since these pieces of equipment have to be in place before your parent comes home, plan ahead. It will take more time than you think.

Unless outside help is available, the care of the patient will fall upon the woman of the house because the man of the house will either be out making a living or pleading incompetence in such matters. Whether you are a sister, daughter, or daughter-in-law, you will end up giving most of the care. Therefore, everything should be done for the convenience of both the caregiver and the cared for.

There will be one thing about the care of an immobile patient that may shock you and may even be worse for your parent. Up to now their bodies and bodily functions were private matters. That will change. In the hospital the nurses were strangers and were trained to be impersonal, but now males may have to be taken care of by female relatives and vice versa. Bodies, entire bodies, will be exposed either by accident or by necessity to persons who did not have that privilege before. The sooner everyone accepts that fact, the easier the care will become. After all, what's the big deal? Facts are facts. Bodies are bodies. Why not treat them with the grace, care, and understanding one would use with a newborn?

The giving of medication, the turning, the exercises, and the attention to his or her bodily functions will occupy a relatively small part of the day and evening. What about the rest of the long hours? Your first step should be to arrange the furniture so that as many of the things he or she will need—such personal items as glasses, books, pictures, water, toilet articles, etc.—will be within reach. Nothing frustrates a bedridden patient more than seeing something he or she wants but can't reach. Also rig up a bell or some simple intercom system for summoning help. It is far better than shouting.

Next, place a TV set at a comfortable viewing position. A remote control unit will save a lot of running around on your part and a lot of unnecessary aggravation on your parent's part, but it is expensive and not available for every set. Television is a good mind distractor for the bedridden, but it does not stimulate much physical activity. So do not forget what I said earlier—and probably what the attending physician also said—about maintaining movement in the joints, about circulation, and about the other necessary bodily functions helped by activity. Remember, all day should not be spent watching soap operas!

A telephone is a handy gadget to widen the world of the handicapped. Since it is difficult to plan for long periods, it might be better to get a long extension cord rather than to have a fixed installation put in by the telephone company. Most hardware stores as well as the new telephone stores have adapters of all sorts that will permit you to rig up temporary telephone service to a sick room with or without a new instrument.

In shops specializing in sick room supplies you will find many helpful gadgets either on display or in catalogs which will be useful in the care of an immobilized parent. For example, there are rubber rings, sheepskin pads, absorbent shields, various holders for eating utensils and toothbrushes, pick-up tongs, restraints, and just about everything handy and necessary for the care and comfort of the disabled. If your parent is under the periodic care of some rehabilitation facility, many of these items will often be suggested or supplied.

Do not overlook those little things necessary for good grooming. Some bedridden patients tend to disregard their personal appearance. You may have observed that you feel better when you are clean, well-groomed, and crisply dressed. So do bedridden patients. Therefore, prevent your parent from becoming an unkempt recluse—unwashed, with long unruly hair, untrimmed nails, and sloppy clothes. Keep a mirror by the bedside or install one nearby so that your father or mother cannot help looking into it. Keep the pressure on for good grooming even if company isn't coming.

Many nursing homes now use "pet therapy," the bringing in of various animals for the handicapped to fondle and react to. Certainly if you have a dog or cat (no snakes or spiders, please), do not put your parent's room off limits. Their wet noses and warm bodies will not do any harm and, in fact, will provide a lot of companionship. Of course, the favorite animal is a grandchild, but I will speak more about those contacts in Chapter 15, "The Gift of Grandchildren."

Remember that regardless of how satisfactory you try to make your parent's environment, the walls will tend to close in. Even with a nice window in the room, much of what is outside will remain unseen. You may bring a few flowers inside, but you cannot bring in a lush hillside or a spring breeze. A piece of sky or a corner of a house is not the whole neighborhood. There will be no horizons painted by a brilliant sunset, no reflections on a still pond, and no bustling crowd if that's what grabs your parent. Must he or she be denied these simple pleasures? Not if you are imaginative. When my father was bedridden in a hospital for close to six months before he died, he was well aware that those faded walls closed in more every day. Since he required a number of semi-emergency trips to and from the hospital in the

months preceding his final stay, he got to know a number of the ambulance attendants. Once in awhile, if they were passing his hospital
room, they would stop in to say "Hello." I am not sure whose idea it
was, but they agreed to take him for a pleasure ride around town on
some clear day. After securing the necessary permissions, they bun-
dled him up on a stretcher, put him in the ambulance, and propped
him up so that he could look out the large side windows. They then
rode around town for about thirty minutes, passing all the places he
loved. What a treat! But you don't need an ambulance. Often a bedridden patient can be placed in the front seat of a car, in a van, or
even in the back of a station wagon on an air mattress or other type of
padding so that he or she can enjoy some favorite sights. It is well
worth the effort and the few gallons of gasoline it might take.

Some patients, although essentially bedridden, do have limited
access to their own room. They can be helped to a chair or commode.
To us a bed is a welcome haven for our weary bones, but for the bedridden it is a prison. Every moment up in a chair is a vacation. Therefore, try to place a comfortable chair close to the bed so with the least
possible help he or she may slide into it. For the lucky ones on the
road to recovery, this may be their first flight from an otherwise
nestlike environment.

Getting Around One's House

You will never see a more unhappy sight in your life than a youngster
who has just learned to crawl being banished to his playpen, even with
all his favorite toys. He wants out! A patient who has been totally
bedridden but who now enjoys some increasing mobility is no different. He wants out! If your parent is in this stage of his or her disability,
the next hurdle will be to move out of his or her room and into the rest
of the house. Remember, your parent has not been able to go to the
refrigerator for a snack, to sit at the dining room table to eat a meal, or
to answer the front door to greet a friend. For him or her, these are
great privileges, so help your parent enjoy them.

His or her degree of mobility will be determined by the extent
and the stage of recovery. Accordingly, your mother or father might
require the use of a wheelchair, a walker, crutches, or a cane. Some
patients might be able to move about by steadying themselves against
the walls or furniture. In many homes, stairs or other obstacles present
insurmountable stumbling blocks to the handicapped. Therefore, at

this time you may find some advantage in changing your parent's room—perhaps from the second floor to the first—provided there are bathroom facilities available. A sun porch or curtained-off dining room, while not fancy, can be converted to such a new function with relative ease. Whatever medical equipment is still needed can follow the patient, as can the intercom. You may remember that I earlier suggested that a telephone not be permanently installed. Now is the time to move it around to wherever your parent wants it.

Before your parent makes his or her first safari, check the placement of your furniture and floor coverings. Throw rugs on slippery floors are an invitation to disaster. A sharp table edge, a protruding lamp, or an unsteady plant are obstacles to be removed. If there are children in the house, set down some new rules about toys or clothes being left on the floor and about running. Unless your parent is confined to a wheelchair, reserve a comfortable chair in the living room for him or her, but make sure that it is one he or she can get in and out of easily.

The pets which were such a help when the patient was bedridden now become a threat unless trained not to jump up on someone who is standing. In addition, the individual must be warned to watch out for small children and animals as both can trip the unsteady.

Your role in caring for someone who is able to get around the house is to normalize his or her activity into the household routine as much as possible and to distribute the added workload between all members of the family, each to his or her own capacity, children included. Certainly, the patient should not be spared responsibility up to his or her own ability.

Many of these patients will enjoy a ride in the country just as much as do the totally bedridden, although their excursions may be more frequent and more varied. Since many elderly are relative homebodies even when in good health, getting around one's house may not be as depressing as one might think and is certainly far more acceptable than being confined to one room.

Getting Around One's Community

The door of opportunity opens further to those who can maneuver outside the home and into the community. The extent to which they can do this on their own will depend upon the degree of residual disability.

Many paraplegics will be confined to wheelchairs, but it is amazing what freedom even this restriction provides. Many are fully employed on the outside or keep house at home. As you would expect, younger individuals learn to get around town with amazing proficiency. Of course, long distances as in rural settings, cold and snow as in the northern climes, hilly terrain as in the mountains, and high-density traffic all mitigate against easy movement. However, access to and within buildings and facilities used by the public is being made easier by laws requiring that they be built according to certain codes promulgated by government, architects, and organizations concerned with the handicapped. As a result, you may have noticed that the curbs on many street corners have been replaced by ramps so that wheelchairs can be maneuvered with greater ease.

Since motorized wheelchairs have come into vogue—I remember getting my father-in-law one when they first became popular in the sixties—the mobility of the elderly has been materially increased. Unfortunately, they are expensive and, unless there are ramps, access is still limited.

Some elderly paraplegics with good shoulder muscles can graduate to crutches. This gives them the ability to drive a car and get around the workplace. I know some physicians who are paraplegics, and I have a neighbor who cuts his own lawn riding on a motorized mower. Unfortunately, most handicapped persons of advanced age are beyond such independence. However, many larger communities have agencies, both profit and nonprofit, which operate special vehicles designed to carry the disabled in their chairs to various public events as well as to medical, dental, and other appointments. Check to see if there is one of these groups in your town. If not, help get one started.

The hemiplegics, those having suffered strokes, present a different and more encouraging picture. Many of these individuals get back to walking albeit a bit shuffling with only a cane for support and balance. They enjoy a far greater freedom than the wheelchair-bound paraplegics because they can maneuver steps, use public transportation, and generally lead a slowed but more normal life. If this represents your parents, you know how much he or she enjoys getting around the community. Make it convenient for your parent.

Getting Around One's Country

Because of the past pressures on your parents to earn a living and to give you and your siblings every advantage they could afford, they probably have not traveled as extensively as they would have liked. Consequently, there may be a pent-up urge to get out and see the rest of this country or to visit faraway friends and relatives. Even if your father was a traveling man and rejoices in the opportunity to sit in his easy chair in front of the TV, your mother might still want to drag him to some of the places he bragged about.

Unfortunately for many, by the time they have the freedom and the funds to travel, they have lost their mobility, and their dreams fall by the wayside. If your parents have the opportunity and desire to travel, do not let them postpone taking that big step. You do not know what tomorrow will bring. Tomorrow may be too late.

Of course, getting around the country by themselves will require more mobility than merely getting around one's town, but there is no reason why your parents should not venture out provided they enjoy reasonably good health. If they can drive and have a reliable vehicle, there is no limit to their ramblings. Many have never flown, but they make the most enthusiastic air travelers. Most airlines tend to give special attention to the elderly. As I have said before, many of these senior citizens have motorhomes or trailers and travel the country over or follow the sun up and down the coasts in their small yachts. Some prefer trains, and following a cross-country train experience of my own I cannot think of a more pleasant and leisurely way to travel. I only wish it had broader national coverage.

Our road, air, and rail systems and our telephone, police, hotel, motel, and health networks provide an excellent umbrella of safety for your mobile parents. Urge them to travel this broad land while they can still enjoy it together. Do not let them use such feeble excuses as being too old or the trip being too expensive. Some parents feel that the more money they spend on travel, the less will be available for your inheritance. Nonsense! Encourage them to be selfish. They earned it—they deserve to spend it. It won't be worth much when you get it anyway.

Getting Around the Whole World

I admit that it is stretching it a bit to discuss world travel in a book on caring for your aging parents. However, if you ever looked into the waiting lounge of an international airline, you would find the average age of the travelers in the same bracket as we have been discussing. I was a member of one such group in which there was a widower up in his nineties who was traveling with a widow well up in her eighties—

yes, in separate rooms. You could not find two more active and congenial people to be with.

Those with minor health problems usually know how to pace themselves. They cut down on the long walking tours and give up much of the after-dinner revelry. Oh, I am sure medical problems do arise, but I have not seen anything major during our six or more foreign trips. In fact, I understand medical emergencies are quite rare. Their pills make it through customs, and they can stick close enough to their diets to make no real difference.

I have a prejudice for escorted tours unless the person is a seasoned traveler with friends at the arriving destination. On such tours there is a guide who knows the ropes and who watches over his or her charges like a mother hen. Furthermore, all the hassle of baggage, rooms, tickets, permits, customs, immigration and a thousand other nasty little details of travel are taken care of. A well-informed travel agent can also steer your parents to many money-saving bargains available to senior citizens throughout the world.

Therefore, my message on world travel by your parents is rather simple. If they are in poor health, urge them not to travel too far. Take them to a travelog movie instead. But if they are reasonably active and healthy, give them a ride to the airport and wish them bon voyage. Of course, make sure they do their preflight planning. Did they pack everything they will need and nothing they would not? You may be a more experienced traveler than your parents, so do not be stingy with your tactful advice.

If this book is ever updated in the next generation, the author might have to include something on space flight. Charles "Pete" Conrad, one of the astronauts who walked on the moon, stated on the TV program "Over Easy" that anybody at any age in reasonably good health should be able to stand the rigors of space travel. But for now, it is nice to know that there is nothing to stop your aging but healthy parents from getting around this one little planet of ours.

CHAPTER 10

Hope
for Health

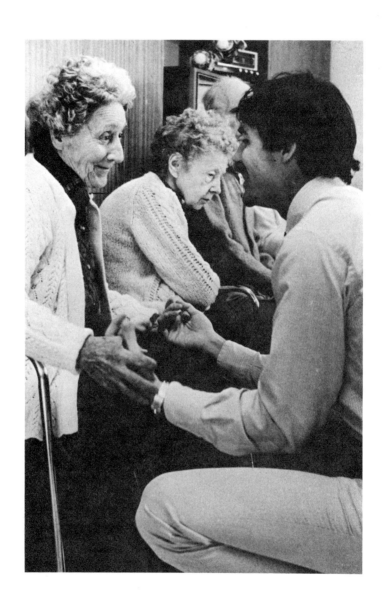

*R*ecently my wife and I have noticed that our children have become more solicitous about our health than ever before. That is only natural; they know the facts, they understand statistics. Their apprehension merely indicates that they are assuming their proper roles as sons and daughters of aging parents. Depending upon your own age and that of your parents, you will sooner or later follow in their footsteps.

Once you have come to grips with your own mortality, you will be possessed by two new concerns: the deterioration of your parents' health and their eventual deaths. Although you might wish to prevent or to postpone these two sad realities, we know that the way your parents eat, work, sleep, and live their lives, and the luck they enjoy along the way will ultimately determine the outcome, not you. Although our bodies do not come with a warranty, there is considerable evidence to suggest that poor health habits lead to an earlier death and that good health habits lead to a longer life.

Consequently, it might be helpful if you knew some of the factors most physicians believe offer the best hope for health and the greatest impact on longevity. There is some chance, even at this late date, that you might be able to influence your parents' lifestyle enough to do some good. Therefore, let me give you my twelve commandments for a long life, although other physicians might shorten or lengthen the list in line with their own research or experience. Incidentally, I know of no one who would place such items in any order of priority. Like the straws that broke the camel's back, no single straw was responsible—it was their cumulative effect.

My twelve commandments for long life are these:

1. Place yourself under the care of a competent physician who will be interested in your total well-being.
2. Eat a varied and nutritionally balanced diet composed of items from all four food groups (meat, dairy, fruits and vegetables, and grain). In addition, limit your consumption of fats, both saturated and unsaturated; restrict your intake of salt and refined sugars; consume more dietary fiber; do not skip breakfast; avoid snacking between meals; and maintain your weight close to the norms for your sex, age, and height. A vegetarian diet is quite acceptable if it includes sufficient dairy products and protein.

3. Participate in regular physical exercise within the limits established by your personal physician.

4. Sleep seven or eight hours each night.

5. Avoid smoking, particularly cigarettes.

6. Avoid all medications not prescribed by your physician; use alcohol sparingly, if at all; and avoid all recreational and addictive drugs.

7. Avoid accidents and health hazards at work, in the home, on the highways and at play by knowing and heeding the potential dangers.

8. Keep mentally alert by remaining inquisitive, by learning new things, by keeping up with current events and by participating in pleasurable activities.

9. Think happy thoughts, laugh and enjoy life. Do not set your expectations so high that you will be constantly disappointed.

10. Manage the expected and the unexpected stresses in your life. Do not bottle up emotional tensions. Relax through rest, recreation, or meditation.

11. Develop a positive attitude toward illness and disability. Do not use your problems either as a crutch or as a means to manipulate or control others.

12. Demonstrate your love to your family and friends. Show your feelings: touch, hug, care, share, and be outgoing, not self-centered.

When you stop and analyze these twelve commandments, you will realize that they are not too difficult to live by. When you realize their benefits, they will seem downright inviting. I have trouble with only one of them, the business about refined sugars, because I love desserts. I keep saying to myself, "Perhaps one small transgression won't do much harm," but I know better. Our ability to metabolize sugar declines as we grow older, and, therefore, sweets could be my downfall—and your parents' as well.

Researchers at the University of California at Berkeley suggest that there might be a link between the health of one older person and that of his or her spouse. Sounds reasonable, but you cannot do much about it other than to use it as an argument should one of your parents refuse to observe these simple commandments. Even so, women outnumber men three to two once they reach sixty-five years of age, and when over eighty-five, the ratio reaches two to one.

Young people tend to think of disease as something you either get over or die from. They overlook chronic illness. Although the national death rate has declined, the long-term disability rate has significantly increased. This trend will eventually influence this country's thinking about every facet of aging from medical research to economics. It cannot happen a moment too soon.

We know that everybody's system undergoes a normal slowing down with age, but not necessarily at a uniform speed. This normal aging process should not be confused with disease although the resulting physiological changes do often promote or lead to disease. In spite of this, the elderly are a pretty hardy bunch. At any point in time some 81 percent of those over sixty-five are fully ambulatory, 95 percent live within their own communities and only 5 percent are confined to hospitals, nursing homes, or other institutions. However, the elderly do see their physicians about 50 percent more often than the younger population. They also are admitted to hospitals about twice as often and usually stay about twice as long. Life expectancy is 68.7 years for males and 76.5 for females, but these are current national averages and have no predictive value for your own parents.

When the rules for a long life eventually fail, as they will, your aging and now ill parents will have hopefully secured the services of a competent physician. Actually, most elderly are treated by a number of physicians. This is quite proper provided each practitioner knows what the other one is doing. Don't laugh. Such confusion happens all too frequently and usually to the patient's disadvantage. Therefore, caution your parents to be frank and open with each physician they see, and do not let them take any medications without the ordering physician knowing what other prescriptions they have been given. But you may ask, "Why is it necessary for my parents to see more than one physician?" Relax, it is for a very good reason. Today the amount of medical knowledge is so vast that it is beyond the capacity of any one person's brain to comprehend. This is why we need specialists. This is why your parents need these special kinds of physicians for many of their complex health problems. However, for their everyday care they should have either a physician in general practice or an internist to provide not only the ongoing care but also to determine if and when a specialist is required.

One of the advantages of having a doctor who is a member of a group practice in which physicians of various disciplines work as partners is the ability to obtain comprehensive care under one roof. Rarely does such a group take economic advantage of a patient or his or her insurance carrier by abusing the use of consultants. However, if the patient asks for a justification for such a consultation and receives a plausible answer, chances are he or she will avoid being referred unnecessarily. Health Maintenance Organizations (HMOs) are merely group practices that offer essentially full health care coverage in and out of the hospital for a predetermined annual sum in contrast to the more traditional system where both the physician and the hospital charge independently for each service rendered.

I would hope that your parents would be able to find a primary-care physician who not only enjoys treating the elderly but who also is skilled in their care. Although I believe medical education and medical practice are improving, as of today not every physician handles elderly patients with equal skill. A recent poll of practicing physicians revealed that although some 12 percent of the population are over sixty-five, only 0.2 percent of doctors regard care of the aged as an important part of their practice. Somebody must be going without.

I admit that the care of older people can be difficult, and that their problems are often not clearly defined. Multiple illnesses confuse the diagnosis. Furthermore, the evaluation of whether a new symptom is life-threatening or merely a passing ache or pain is difficult to determine with certainty. The physician prefers not to put the patient through inconvenient and expensive tests unnecessarily, yet he or she does not want to miss anything and so is faced with a dilemma. But that is the physician's problem. Yours is to see that your parents are under the care of a physician who is comfortable with old people and who knows enough about the process of aging to go beyond just writing a prescription. A good physician should be interested in their lifestyle, in their emotional problems, in their financial pressures and, in fact, in everything that may in any way impact upon their health. He or she should be willing to spend enough time with your parents to work through their complaints. If their doctor listens to their hearts through their overcoats, blames everything on old age, and writes a prescription after a five-minute visit, suggest to your parents that they change doctors. They are being shortchanged.

Furthermore, the physician ought to be willing to refer your parents to a specialist if he or she is either unsure of what is going on or lacks the skill to handle the condition properly. Although not all physicians like to do that, if you think the time has come for your mother or father to get a second opinion, talk it over with the physician. Unless you get a convincing answer, get one.

While it is understandably difficult to get a physician to make house calls, an increasing number of gerontologists will see terminally ill patients in their homes in order to prevent such individuals from being transferred to either a hospital or a nursing home for proper care. Most hospice programs provide such home visits, particularly when the hospice nurse deems it necessary.

There are two innovative concepts of delivering ambulatory health care that your parents might find useful. Both are freestanding facilities operated either by physicians or by hospitals, and they are usually located in or near suburban shopping centers. Most remain open only from dawn to dusk but do so every day, holidays included. The first is called an "urgent care center" or some similar name and caters to walk-in patients with minor emergencies. The other type expands on this concept by adding to its emergency service some continuity of care by scheduling appointments for return visits, thereby acting more like a small family practice clinic. Although these two programs have a limited place in your parents' care, as does the hospital emergency room, they do not take the place of the effective and interested physician skilled in geriatric medicine.

I trust that you are now convinced that your parents should be under the continuing care of a competent physician. Yet I have known elderly individuals, educated and affluent at that, who will only see their physician when things get unbearable. That's not right! Many potentially serious conditions can be discovered on a routine examination when the patient is still asymptomatic and curable. The dosages or choice of drugs may have to be modified. Furthermore, if an acute problem does come up in the middle of the night, it is helpful to have the patient's baseline data available. So should one or both of your parents shun routine medical care because of ignorance, braggadocio, fear, or even financial reasons, urge them to seek attention immediately.

Some large hospitals or teaching institutions operate Centers for Assessment and Care of the Elderly, which attempt to maximize each person's quality of life through a complete evaluation of the individual's medical and social problems. Referrals are usually through physicians or social agencies, but follow-up services are performed by the patient's own physician. If you suspect a problem and one of these centers is near you, suggest to your mother or father that it be discussed with his or her physician.

Although traditional medicine has in the past concentrated on treating illness, there is a growing emphasis inside and outside of organized medicine on promoting wellness. As a result, a number of alternative health care systems have sprung up. Nurse practitioners operating independently of any physician offer such wellness services as health examinations, blood pressure checks, immunizations, health education, and counseling. Other practitioners offer wholistic medicine, which emphasizes the spiritual and social forces influencing health. Still others advocate physical fitness and a healthy lifestyle. Now, I do not wish to disparage these efforts because there is much merit in each approach. And while most overlap with traditional medicine, I want to stress that they should be added to the care provided by a physician, not substituted for it. Although we may still have some problems with the current health care system in this country, there is no doubt that modern medicine has produced the highest quality of health care the world has ever known. Therefore, do not let your parents miss out on it.

I am optimistic about the future of medicine, particularly about the scientific progress. There are miracles ahead that we cannot even dream of today. However, I am not as optimistic about the health workforce. At the moment we have ample physicians, but their distribution and the numbers of those interested in geriatric medicine are not encouraging. I am even less sanguine about the supply of nurses and other hands-on health care professionals for the future. The number of female nursing graduates is decreasing as the opportunities for women in general employment are increasing. Furthermore, efforts at cost control may depress the numbers even more. Consequently, these pressures may put you and your family back into the nursing business as were your forebears when they provided much of the care for their aging parents within their own homes.

Once your parents are under the care of a competent physician, and once you begin to recognize that you may be one of the caregivers, what medical conditions will likely cause your parents trouble as the years go by? Of the more than 1,000 major diseases and their subgroups listed in the International Classification of Diseases, the elderly are subject to every one except for a few congenital malformations and conditions peculiar to childhood. As I hinted earlier, few older people will have a single disease. They are more likely to have one or more chronic conditions which may or may not be under active treatment at the time they develop something new. Hypertension, arthritis, diabetes, prostatic hypertrophy, gallstones, hernia, hemorrhoids, loss of visual or hearing acuity, skin problems, old injuries, arteriosclerosis, obesity, lung disease, and mental illness are just a few examples. In turn, some of the pressing problems your parents will develop will be complications or extensions of these chronic diseases. Cataracts, heart disease, and urinary retention are good examples. Most of the elderly's new problems will be coincidental to their chronic problems, while others may be complicated by them. So be prepared for any and every conceivable combination.

In spite of the potential diversity of illnesses, the most common medical condition and the one most likely to cause death for those sixty-five and over is that group of diseases lumped under the broad heading of *cardiovascular diseases.* These are the diseases of the heart and blood vessels. Trailing some distance behind in frequency are malignancies, or cancers, followed still further by respiratory infections, accidents, and diabetes. All others follow with small or fractional percentages. Which will affect your parents, no one knows. The law of averages fails when you deal with only one individual. Therefore, you and your parents will have to live a day at a time and take whatever comes along. The universal prayer, "If I could only know what to expect," will remain unanswered.

I do not want to convert this chapter into a do-it-yourself medical textbook of the most common medical problems your aging parents might experience. Yet, I want to help you understand enough of what might happen to them so that you can better care for them when the need arises. Consequently, as a compromise I shall run through a dozen or so of the most likely conditions that might face your aging parents.

Incontinence

Although incontinence is a symptom, not a disease, it merits first consideration, because families can handle almost any other problem in the home. In fact, it is the final insult that causes many patients to be transferred to a nursing home. It is estimated that as many as 5 percent to 10 percent of those over sixty-five who are living at home are incontinent. Although urinary incontinence is most common, bowel incontinence is the most difficult to handle. It certainly is in infants, and it is more so with adults. Yet unlike the infant, incontinence is not only a problem for the caregiver, but it is also a great embarrassment to the patient.

Incontinence can be classified as temporary or fixed and can be caused by a dozen or more specific diseases or mechanical problems. Therefore, it should be investigated thoroughly by your parent's physician. A specific cause should be identified and a decision made as to how it should be treated or, at least, managed. Do not let anyone pass it off as just part of old age. It is not! There is a cause which may be amenable to medical or surgical treatment. If not, there are drugs, mechanical devices, behavior modification, and other techniques to make it more manageable.

Although persistent vomiting cannot be considered incontinence, the problem it creates for the caregiver is quite similar. Usually the condition is of relatively short duration; however, it should be evaluated by a physician. It may be due to some medication he or she has prescribed or to some threatening, new condition.

Senility

No other problem of aging causes so much fear and apprehension both to the elderly and to their families as does senile dementia, commonly called *senility*. By definition, senility is the development, usually gradual, of widespread intellectual impairment resulting in loss of memory, inability to concentrate, increased difficulty with numbers, restlessness, repetitive meaningless actions, depression, and loss of orientation for time and place. Some may progress into delirium with marked confusion, delusions, and even hallucinations. In addition to the deterioration of intellect, there are generally personality changes such as irritability and a diminished sense of humor. Some may lose their ability to speak, feed themselves, or control their bodily functions. It is not a pretty picture.

But be careful not to let your parents think that their periodic forgetfulness, particularly of names or of insignificant details, is a sure sign of senility. It is not. Most older people have intermittent lapses of memory for recent minor events. That is normal aging, not senility, so do not worry about it.

It has been estimated that approximately 10 percent of our population over sixty-five years of age shows some signs of true senility. That may be a small percentage, but when translated into absolute numbers, it represents over two million individuals. No section of society, no ethnic group, no economic class is immune.

Senility, while associated with old age, is not a part of the normal process of aging. It is a disease; more accurately, the result of many diseases. Cases can be classified into four types:

1. *Alzheimer's disease*, accounting for approximately 50 percent of the cases, is the most severe of the four types of senility and

is characterized by a progressive and debilitating dementia leading to death in five to ten years. The diagnosis must be made by elimination, although altered CAT scans of the brain are suggestive. The only proof of the disease is by microscopic examination of the brain after death. If its progress is slow and mild enough, the patient may so adapt to his or her handicap that it hardly shows. However, some 75,000 unfortunate individuals succumb to this tragic disease each year. At the present time there is no cure, but it has been predicted that current research efforts will control the disease within ten years.

2. *Multi-infarct dementia,* accounting for approximately 25 percent of the cases, is caused by multiple small strokes or cloggings of the blood vessels which supply the brain with needed blood. Deprived of oxygen, the cells die, causing small infarcts. Since nerve cells do not regenerate, a person who suffers many infarcts will eventually become senile. Treatment of the underlying blood vessel disease may retard or prevent further progression of the infarcts, and, therefore, of the senility itself.

3. Symptoms of senility, accounting for approximately 20 percent of the cases, can be traced to drug intoxication, malnutrition, or the secondary effects of other illnesses, particularly depression. If these are corrected, the symptoms of senility usually disappear.

4. Approximately 5 percent of the cases are due to causes that remain unknown even after thorough investigation.

Unfortunately, Alzheimer's disease and most other incapacitating neurological illnesses create tremendous social problems. If you are unlucky enough to be the caregiver of an aging parent with advanced senile dementia, your life will be changed. However, more often the spouse, if living, is the caregiver and his or her life will also be changed. To tend to such patients is a twenty-four-hour physical and emotional drain. The individuals require constant attention, yet return little or no recognition or appreciation. They forget; they wander; they repeat meaningless actions; they lose judgment; and they no longer are able to handle their own affairs. It is like taking care of a stranger or even an unpredictable robot. There is little opportunity to communicate, to share affection, or even to please. Nevertheless, the patient deserves his or her dignity, independence, and autonomy to the maximum degree possible.

It is little wonder that half of the patients in nursing homes are victims of senile dementia. Because nursing home care is so expensive, many families are left with a tragic dilemma. The patient is too difficult to care for at home, yet care in an appropriate institution is not possible because the patient is not eligible for public support. So what happens? It becomes a family problem. Sharing the care among a number of family members helps, of course. So does respite care, which provides temporary admission of the patient to an appropriate facility in order to give the caregivers some needed rest. Yet in spite of all these difficulties, we see an amazing performance by many families. They are to be commended. But to be honest I must admit that the burden of caring for a severely senile parent is a heavy burden.

The Alzheimer's Disease and Related Disorders Association is a national organization (telephone 800-621-0379) that provides information and support services to families caring for such patients. Check to see if there is a local chapter of ADRDA in your area. If so, it may be of help. If not, you might wish to start one.

Malignancies

Most people are terrorized by the word *cancer.* In part, they are right, but mostly they are wrong. It has been said with some factual basis that everyone dies from cancer unless they die from something else first. Yet cancer is no longer the threat to life it once was. Cure rates are constantly being improved. Many malignancies are definitely curable, and once treatment is completed, the patients lead long and healthy lives.

Technically, all cancers are malignancies, but not all malignancies are cancer. However, this is of little practical importance unless you are confused by the terminology the physician uses. Both cancer and malignancies are abnormal growths of body cells which often metastasize or spread to distant parts of the body through the blood or lymph streams, and which if untreated or untreatable, lead to death. Except for certain rare childhood tumors, cancer is an age-related condition—that is, it increases in frequency after middle-age. Although science has identified certain carcinogens (cancer-causing substances), the cause of most malignancies is still unknown. Diet, smoking, certain chemicals, sunlight, even lifestyles have been

implicated. Apparently certain ill-defined internal or host susceptibil-
ities must also be present before disease occurs.

Cancer is not one disease; it is many. Malignancies can affect
every organ in the body including the blood cells. The symptoms,
treatment, and prognosis vary not only with the organ involved but
also with the type and grade (the virulence) of the malignancy, since
different types can involve the same organ. They also vary according
to the stage of the disease; the earlier it is discovered and treated, the
better the results.

Consequently, your primary concern is to urge your parents to be
observant to changes in their bodies and in the way they function. A
good method of introducing this touchy subject is to obtain from your
local chapter of the American Cancer Society their excellent, free
brochure entitled "Listen to Your Body." It lists cancer's seven warning signals:

1. Change in bowel or bladder habits
2. A sore that does not heal
3. Unusual bleeding or discharge
4. Thickening or lump in breast or elsewhere
5. Indigestion or difficulty in swallowing
6. Obvious change in wart or mole
7. Nagging cough or hoarseness

In addition, the brochure expands on each of these warning signals
and briefly describes thirteen of the most common cancers that can be
diagnosed early if an individual heeds the signals and promptly reports
them to his or her physician. Incidentally, you should also heed these
seven signals. They apply to every age group.

Every physician can recite dozens of cases in which a person with
a curable cancer delayed treatment until it was too late. And these are
not stupid people. A nurse I knew who was an operating room supervi-
sor ignored obvious signs of a breast tumor until it was too late. Why,
I'll never know. We hear so many feeble excuses: fear of mutilation,
the discomfort of chemotherapy, and the remark "I didn't think it was
serious." Don't let your parents fall into one of these traps. Life is more
precious than that! Remember, cancer is no longer a death warrant;
rather it is an invitation to treatment.

For those of you who may be the caregiver to a patient with terminal cancer, be mindful of two problems. The first is the patient's

knowledge of the eventual outcome and the long time he or she usually has to contemplate it. This can trigger depression and all sorts of reactionary behavior. The second is the fear of pain which can be a nasty part of some cancers. With modern drugs and methods of administration, this should be of no concern. Most physicians will reassure a patient of this at the appropriate time. I will mention the hospice movement in Chapter 13, "Homes Away from Home." It is designed for just such patients.

Cardiovascular Diseases

Unlike cancer, senility, and many of the diseases causing incontinence, the *cardiovascular diseases* have a certain respectability in the eyes of our society. It was not too long ago that many surviving relatives asked physicians not to use such diagnoses as cancer on a patient's death certificate. They wanted no written record of the truth. Yet I've never heard anyone make the same request in cases of cardiovascular disease. How many times have your friends given you the gory details of their heart attack, but only vague references to their condition if they had cancer of the bladder? Apparently, some of the same prejudice persists.

Yet similar to cancer, the cardiovascular diseases comprise a whole constellation of different conditions. Some can lead to sudden death, as in the case of a myocardial infarction (heart attack); others result in long periods of disability, as in the case of a cerebrovascular accident (stroke); while others, such as hypertension, will not materially affect longevity provided they are caught and brought under treatment early enough. This broad group of cardiovascular diseases can produce a wide spectrum of symptoms including pain, shortness of breath, weakness, paralysis, dizziness, cold hands and feet, loss of memory, cyanosis, kidney failure, fever, and dozens of others. Consequently, it is imperative to have the exact diagnosis determined in order that the proper therapy be started. Usually the treatment is medical, but occasionally it's surgical.

Most cardiovascular diseases share four common characteristics:

1. They generally can be prevented or significantly reduced in severity by observing a healthy lifestyle.
2. They generally respond to treatment if diagnosed early.
3. They generally require the continuation of treatment for the rest of the patient's life.
4. They generally get progressively worse if not treated.

Should your aging parents suffer from one of these diseases, the most significant consideration for you is to make sure that they follow their physician's orders. As mentioned, most therapies include a lifelong drug routine and an altered lifestyle. Because these illnesses extend over such prolonged periods, and because patients see and feel no rapid deterioration, many people tend to stop their medications or take them only when they have a bad day. That routine will not work. The disease process will continue its insidious damage. If you think your parents are the kind who will obey instructions to the letter, don't worry. They will take care of themselves. But if they are careless, forgetful, or tend to be the bravado type, step in and help them set up a foolproof routine. I will mention at the end of this chapter a number of ways by which you can help your parents keep to their medication schedule. But for now, let me just say that if they live with you, check on their performance. Do not take the responsibility away from them unless they are patently incompetent, as that would be emotionally devastating. But you can still be their monitor. If they live separately, phone them right after the medications are due. They will get the message.

Most patients with cardiovascular disease do well at home, although some may need nursing assistance depending on their degree of disability. Some will require hospitalization for relatively brief periods. A few will require nursing home care, not so much because of the nature of their disease, but because there is no one at home to take care of them properly. If your mother or father lives alone but requires care, you will have to balance that need with his or her unbelievable zeal for independence. I witnessed that urge to go home and be independent in an elderly gentleman lying on the floor of a barber shop with a team of paramedics working over him. What optimism! Because the disability from cardiovascular disease lasts so long, few of these patients are eligible for hospice care.

Since these diseases are so debilitating, most cardiac patients need strong but restrained support. Overprotection can make cardiac cripples of individuals who need activity, and, in turn, imprudent activity can be harmful to those with little cardiac reserve. Your parents' doctor should guide you in these matters. Anything that drags on for such an extended period can produce depression and frustration. Be imaginative in keeping your parents happy, useful, and loved. Give them all the emotional support you can muster.

Incidentally, knowledge of CPR (cardiopulmonary resuscitation) is desirable for everyone, but particularly for those with relatives with coronary artery disease. Ask your local Red Cross chapter or rescue squad about training programs in your area. CPR saves lives! It could save not only your aging parents' lives, but the life of anyone with whom you come in contact during those dreadful few moments of cardiac arrest.

Mental Illness

You may look at your aging parents with awe. They have faced every conceivable problem of life: growing up, getting married, raising a family, earning a living, fighting wars, and facing all sorts of economic hardships. Yet they have come through with flying colors, confident and emotionally able to take it on the chin. If they have not developed emotional problems by now, it would seem logical that they would not do so in the few years they have remaining. However, the later years bring a whole new set of vexing challenges. Retirement, the loss of a spouse, one's own impending death, the deterioration of one's appearance and physical abilities, financial problems, moving from the homestead, and many other similar hurdles continue to expose your parents to a host of emotional problems at a time when they are least able to fight back.

As I have mentioned in previous chapters and will again and again, your parents are prime candidates for depression, the most common emotional problem we see in the upper years. If one or even both of your parents seem overburdened by real or imagined problems of daily living, lack their usual energy and ability to cope, can't sleep, won't eat, and become excessively dependent, they may be victims of depression. What is more, they might take out their helplessness, bitterness, and frustrations on you by demanding sympathy and blaming you for their troubles.

But before you play amateur psychiatrist, check to see how much of their day-to-day living is really depressing. Are they being treated fairly as adults? Is their environment conducive to a normal, happy life? Are there any reversible medical problems? Can they justifiably mimic Rodney Dangerfield in saying, "I get no respect"? Maybe their lives are depressing. Maybe they are right in feeling the way they do. You do not need a psychiatrist to spice up their lives or to give them meaning. That is within your reach.

However, if their behavior seems beyond the normal ups and downs we all experience, and if you have done everything in your power to correct the obvious, then talk it over with whichever parent seems depressed. If there is a spouse, involve him or her in the discussion. It is possible that your parent could be upset by something easily correctable once you uncover it. However, if it seems more serious than that, more pathologic, suggest that your parent seek help from his or her personal physician. In many cases, the physician should be able to clear up the problem through counseling and medication. If not, he or she may suggest psychiatric care. Unfortunately, many of the elderly have a prejudice against psychiatry and will resist any such offer. If fact, they might even get more vitriolic in the process. If this tack does not work, try to have your parent talk to a clergyman or even to a trusted friend. If you think that will not work, try the reverse and suggest that one of their friends take the initiative and talk to your parent. If the problem persists and behavior so deteriorates that your parent becomes a threat to him- or herself or to others, you have little choice but to consult a physician or social agency on how to proceed. Remember, suicide is most common in people over fifty who suffer from depression. But do not let it get that far. Do not assume when someone threatens suicide that he or she is just trying to get attention. That may be true, but then again it may not be. However, do not panic. Consult your parent's physician and accept his or her advice.

Unfortunately, the elderly are not immune to other emotional problems such as phobia, anxiety, paranoia, hypochondria, compulsive behavior, neurasthenia, any of the psychosomatic illnesses, and even the more serious psychoses that require institutionalization. Although less frequent than simple depression, these disease states must be kept in mind. It is very difficult for a family member to distinguish between normal aging, senility, and the symptoms of these other specific emotional disorders. This is particularly so in the early stages. When full-blown, almost anyone can tell normal behavior from abnormal. The skill is to catch the process early enough so that if it is reversible, treatment can begin.

Mental illness can be frightening. However, it should not be kept in the closet. It will not go away by itself. It is not a normal part of aging. It is an illness that requires prompt and competent treatment as any other disease. Unfortunately, the patient will not recognize it. There is no pressure for him or her to seek relief as there is with pain. So if mental illness strikes one of your parents, particularly if there is no spouse, his or her care will be your responsibility. You will have to take charge.

Diabetes

I doubt if there is an adult in this country who does not recognize the word *diabetes* and who does not know someone suffering from it. Yet I also doubt if most of them have their facts straight unless, of course, they are diabetics themselves.

Diabetes mellitus, its scientific name, is a noncontagious disease caused by the failure of certain "islet" cells in the pancreas to produce enough of the hormone, insulin, which the body needs to convert the sugar found in one's diet into energy. Consequently, as the amount of unused sugar in the blood increases, the kidneys try to get rid of it by excessive production of urine. This in turn causes thirst and more uri-nation. The excess sugar is easily detected in both the urine and the blood. The disease, of course, causes other problems, such as weight loss, fatigue, decreased resistance to infections, itching of the genitals, and a host of serious complications.

If one of your parents is a diabetic, it is possible that he or she developed the disease during childhood, but it is much more likely that it appeared in middle-age or later. If it has been long-standing or is severe, chances are he or she is taking daily insulin injections. If it appeared late in life, it may be controlled by diet and weight reduction alone. Regardless of time of onset or severity, all diabetics should be under the constant care of a physician who will monitor the progress of the disease and adjust medication dosages accordingly.

Your role in your parent's care may be insigificant or crucial, de-pending on whether or not your parent is living with you. If you are the one who does the cooking and serving for an extended family, you should learn the rules for a diabetic diet. Sources for such information include your parent's doctor, a hospital dietician, the local chapter of the American Diabetes Association, or literature from your library or bookstore.

If your parent is blind or severely incapacitated yet requires insu-lin, you or someone else will have to administer the injections and test the urine on whatever schedule the physician prescribes. Again, the physician will see that you have the proper instructions.

In a diabetic there are two life-threatening conditions, both end-ing in coma and death if not handled properly. If your parent lives with you, you must be on the lookout for these possibilities. If he or she does not live with you, there is little you can do except check the best way you can to assure yourself that your parent is living by the rules. The first of these emergencies is *insulin shock,* caused by too much insulin in relation to the dietary intake. This results in tremors, cold sweats, excessive hunger, and eventually coma. The absence of sugar in the urine of a diabetic is a sure sign of excess insulin. A glass of sweetened orange juice or a few lumps of sugar will usually straighten things out quickly. The second is *diabetic acidosis,* the reverse of insulin shock—not enough insulin. Yet it is not that simple. Infections, surgery, even dental extractions can throw a person sufficiently out of insulin balance to cause acidosis. Therefore, during these stressful times, close control of sugar levels must be maintained. Some early symptoms of diabetic acidosis are severe thirst, dryness of skin and tongue, nausea and vomiting, and deep breathing. If not treated promptly with insulin, coma will surely follow. If this does happen, or if it appears imminent, rush your parent to the hospital. This is truly a medical emergency.

You may have heard that diabetics eventually develop cataracts, gangrene, and other nasty complications, but that is not universally true. For now, concentrate on not letting your parent's diabetes get out of control even for a single day.

If your parent does not wear a diabetic identification bracelet or necklace, give him or her one. You will never know when it will help save his or her life. A simple identification card is used by some diabetics, but I do not believe it gives the same protection because it takes a clothing search to find it. Many strangers either do not think to look or would prefer not to go through someone else's pockets.

While you are worrying about your parent, why don't you have yourself checked over, particularly if you are the blood descendent of the patient? There is a slim chance that the tendency for diabetes might be inherited.

Remember, once a diabetic, always a diabetic. As the years roll by, the treatment necessary to control your parent's disease will probably change. It is also true that a nondiabetic may become a diabetic, so stay vigilant.

Before I leave this subject let me erase any confusion you might have between the terms *diabetes mellitus* and *diabetes insipidus.* They are two separate diseases with nothing in common except the symptoms of thirst and voluminous urination. Diabetes insipidus, a rather rare condition, is caused by insufficient production of a pituitary hormone, not insulin. It is easily treated by hormone replacement therapy.

Arthritis

The term *arthritis* is in the active lexicon of every elderly person, yet not everyone who complains about it has it. This is because the term has degenerated from its correct definition of an inflammation of a joint to one that embraces a host of related rheumatic disorders in the structures surrounding the joints such as tendons, ligaments, and bursae.

However, the complaints we hear are not all that unjustified. It is estimated that approximately fifty million Americans have some form of arthritis and that about half of them suffer sufficiently to require medical attention. In fact, most people over the age of sixty have enough arthritis to be detected by X-ray.

Included in the true joint diseases are:

1. *Osteoarthritis*, also called *degenerative joint disease*, which is the most common form of chronic arthritis and is caused by wear and tear on the joints and is understandably associated with advancing age

2. *Traumatic arthritis*, which is an acute condition caused by an injury to the joint that may or may not give problems in later life

3. *Rheumatoid arthritis*, which is a potentially crippling manifestation of a serious and chronic systemic disease that usually starts in early adulthood

4. *Infectious arthritis*, which is a rare but usually temporary condition

5. *Gout*, which is a relatively infrequent metabolic disorder producing pain and swelling of the joints, often in the big toe

6. *Spondylitis*, which is a rare disorder fusing the joints of the backbone and resulting in a stiff or "poker" spine

In addition, there are the disorders of the structures around the joints such as tendinitis, bursitis, capsulitis, slipped disks, and plain old backache. You can forget the few other conditions which can affect the joints and which may or may not be classified as arthritis.

Do not try to diagnose or treat your aging parents' aches and pains. Their physician should do that. If it is arthritis, he or she should also outline a course of treatment which usually involves more than just a prescription. In most cases, while a cure is not possible, alleviation of the painful symptom is. Recent advances in surgery using artifi-cial replacement joints in hips, knees, and fingers have been highly successful, and the immediate return of function is almost miraculous.

Except for listening to your aging parents' complaints and suffer-ing vicariously as you see them shuffling around in obvious discomfort, your role in their care will be minimal. If they are severely crippled, you may have to assist them as you would if they were equally handicapped by any other disabling disease. I will cover more on this in Chapter 17, "Three Ways to Cope."

Unfortunately, but understandably, arthritis has had a bad press. The elderly fear it because they have heard about its pain and disabil-ity from TV. Yet few suffer intense pain or are really incapacitated to any severe degree. So buoy up their spirits. Remind them to continue taking their medications. Encourage them to keep active (except dur-ing the acute episodes when their physician may prescribe rest). Try to prevent the depression that often follows when the diagnosis is first made. Arthritis is indeed a pain, but it is not a killer.

Osteoporosis

While we are on bones, it only seems appropriate to mention *osteopo-rosis*, which in simple terms means "porous bones." This disorder may well strike your mother if she isn't careful. It is a condition of un-known origin striking primarily, but not exclusively, thin-boned, light-skinned, postmenopausal women who have not been exposed to heavy physical exercise. Men can get osteoporosis, but it usually oc-curs much later in life than for women. The bones lose their strength and density and, as a result, are prone to break with the slightest fall or even overexertion. Unfortunately, one in four of these older women will develop osteoporosis, and usually before they reach their seventieth birthday one in three of these will suffer a fracture of their wrists, hips, or whatever bone is put under stress. Often small fractures occur in the softened spine, which after time tends to compress. As a result, these women get noticeably shorter, often with a distinct cur-vature of the spine sometimes referred to as the "dowager's hump." One of the first indications of the disease may be loosening of the teeth because of the softening of the jaw bone.

Whether your mother lives with you or far away, try to protect her from falls. But odds are that she will still trip, bump into some-thing, or make a quick move that will result in a fracture. Fortunately, such fractures heal without too much difficulty. Hip fractures, which used to be treated by heavy plaster casts and required dangerous and prolonged periods of convalescence, are now treated by surgery with excellent results.

Although it is best to avoid such bone loss by an adequate intake of calcium throughout one's life, there is still some hope for the aging osteoporosis-prone individual. Most authorities recommend a three-pronged attack:

1. An adequate intake of calcium, either through a high calcium diet—milk and dairy products being excellent natural sources of calcium—or supplemental calcium in the form of calcium tablets
2. Regular weight-bearing exercise, such as walking
3. The avoidance of caffeine, smoking, and diets excessively high in protein because there appears to be some unexplained but deleterious relationship between these practices and osteoporosis

Vitamin D and certain hormones may also be recommended in special cases. However, there is no sure and quick reversal of this disease once it has set in, although some new research gives promise.

There is a tendency for patients with osteoporosis to give up all activity in fear of having an accident. Make sure they are careful, yes, but don't let your parents become inactive. Bones need exercise as much as muscles.

Parkinson's Disease or Parkinsonism

When an actor portrays an elderly character, he or she will walk with a stiff, shuffling gait, slightly bent over as if falling forward, hands and fingers twitching, as if rolling pills, head nodding rhythmically, and face held masklike and unsmiling with the eyebrows elevated. When speaking, his or her lips will move in a slow, deliberate manner. By so doing, the actor will be accurately mimicking Parkinsonism. Unfortunately, the actor will make one mistake. He or she will tend to portray the character as being slow-witted. That is just not so. In spite of Parkinsonism being a disease of the brain, the mind is unaffected.

Parkinsonism is not uncommon, yet you will see fewer cases on the streets today than in the past because there are now drugs that effectively control the symptoms. Consequently, many victims can continue to work or keep house without too much difficulty. As in many other conditions affecting the elderly, its onset is rather insidious. In fact, you may notice it before your parents do. If so, suggest that they consult their physician immediately. Once on medication, see that they continue it faithfully, because the symptoms will reappear if the treatment is stopped.

Decubitus Ulcer

If you are the principal caregiver to a bedridden or wheelchair-bound parent, you will have to learn a number of nursing techniques in order to meet his or her bodily needs and to keep the bed or chair environment clean and serviceable. Your local Red Cross chapter should be able to either teach you or help you find adequate instruction.

One problem in the care of such patients is the prevention of *decubitus ulcers*, or bedsores. These are caused by constant pressure of the patient's body against the bed or chair. In effect, his or her weight squeezes the blood vessels in those areas, shutting off the blood supply for sufficiently long periods to cause the skin and underlying tissues to die, resulting in an ulcer.

Although there might be a few exceptions, in general the development of a bedsore shows poor care. Any nurse will tell you that bedsores are easier to prevent than to heal. Consequently, you should observe the following four simple rules:

1. Distribute the patient's weight so that all of it does not rest on the buttocks, heels, elbows, or other bony prominences. This can be done by frequent turning and using pillows, rubber rings, sheepskin pads, or a device called an "alternating pressure mattress." If your parent has some use of his or her muscles, encourage frequent turning and exercise.

2. Keep the bed or chair pad clean and free from wrinkles. Avoid rubber sheets.

3. Keep the skin clean and dry by using alcohol and talcum after bathing and turning. Expose the skin to the air as much as possible.

4. If the skin appears red or sore, protect it by a rubber ring or surgical doughnut. If the redness persists, report it to the patient's physician.

Decubitus ulcers are unpleasant physically and emotionally. Do everything in your power to prevent them.

Respiratory Infections

Colds, bronchitis, influenza, and even pneumonia are no different in older people than in a younger age group. The difference is in the patient. What may be a mere annoyance to you may be fatal to your parent. Most elderly people have less respiratory reserve, less efficient immune systems necessary to fight infections, greater intolerance to certain drugs, and exhibit other systemic differences that make them more vulnerable to otherwise ordinary respiratory diseases.

Consequently, exposure to those already ill should be avoided if possible, and early signs of any such illness should be reported to their physician. If your sick parent lives apart from you, insist that he or she consult a physician promptly. Procrastination or self-medication is not the treatment of choice for a respiratory infection in an elderly individual. Most of us older physicians remember the days before antibiotics when pneumonia claimed so many lives. It can still do so if the patient is not promptly and competently treated.

Herpes Zoster

Herpes zoster, commonly called "shingles," is an unusual infection caused by a virus that has probably been lying dormant in the cells of one or more nerves since an attack of chicken pox in childhood. It is characterized by small, painful blisters of the skin or mucous membrane along the route of the affected nerves. It occurs most frequently on the trunk, but not exclusively. The rash usually appears after a brief period of nonspecific illness. Its only significance to you as the caregiver is to know of its existence since there is some evidence that it occurs more frequently in the elderly and in those who are chronically ill. Your parent's physician should be called.

Herpes zoster is not contagious unless the caregiver has never had chicken pox, and then it is no more contagious than when taking care of a child with chicken pox. So don't be fearful. Just keep your hands and the patient's bedclothing and environment clean.

Accidents and Acute Pain

As I indicated earlier, accidents hold a serious threat for your parents. Poor vision, inadequate hearing, arthritis, lessened sense of balance, and general weakness all contribute to the frequency of accidents involving the elderly. Most of these accidents will occur in your parents' own home, some in yours, some in public buildings, and some in the street. Accidents will be discussed in more detail in Chapter 14, "Playing It Safe." But meanwhile, remember two things. Try to prevent accidents, and have a plan of action worked out in advance should one occur.

Pain is the body's way of telling one that something is wrong. If you accept the fact that as your parents age they will also develop more medical problems, then you can be forewarned that acute pain will someday disturb your parents' normal routine and, after a frantic phone call, yours as well. Do not take their pain lightly. If it is severe and persistent or is accompanied by such symptoms as nausea and vomiting, sweating, pallor, lethargy, or intensification of the pain, get your parent to a hospital fast. Call the ambulance, rescue squad, or emergency medical van—whichever your community has available. If the distance is short, you may drive him or her yourself, but if the emergency medical technicians can get there more quickly, call them. They can start emergency treatment on the spot. Remember, a patient begins to get better or worse from the moment of onslaught. There are no holding patterns, so act with dispatch. As with accidents, have a plan of action worked out in advance. Things will go better if you do.

Hypothermia, or low body temperature, is neither an accident nor acute pain per se, but it can present both an emergency and a threat. Your parents are much more sensitive to cold than you are. Their circulatory and temperature-control mechanisms do not respond as effectively as when they were younger. As a result, hypothermia can cause severe damage. Therefore, help your aging parents avoid prolonged exposure to cold whether it be while walking, shoveling snow, sitting at some outdoor sporting event, or hunting and fishing. The inability to move about when they are confined in a seat, boat, or hunting blind compounds the problem. If the wind is blowing, they might also suffer frostbite more quickly due to the wind-chill. Of course, occupying a poorly heated home is an invitation to disaster.

Your parents are equally sensitive to excessively high temperatures, which can lead to *heat exhaustion* or *heat stroke*, both dangerous to the elderly. Are your parents exposing themselves to these twin dangers either willingly or unwillingly? If you do not know, find out. Then, warn them of the dangers.

Taking Medications

Throughout this chapter I have repeatedly suggested that you try to assure yourself that your parents are taking their medications properly. This is particularly important because many of the drugs they take will be required for the rest of their lives. Consequently, let me mention a few tricks that should help establish some orderly routines regardless of whether your parents take their own medications or whether you or other caregivers are forced to administer them yourselves.

The easiest way is to time them to some other household activity, such as the morning toilet, mealtimes, or bedtime. Keeping the containers visible rather than in a medicine cabinet or drawer will also jog one's memory. A shelf near the kitchen or bathroom sink is handy.

I like the plastic seven-day pill reminders. Each compartment has a cover marked with a separate day of the week. They come in different sizes to accommodate different sizes and numbers of tablets. It is possible to use two or more containers in different colors to accommodate medications taken at different times of the day. Some people remind themselves by placing their pills in a small glass or plastic container next to the kitchen sink or some other frequented spot. If your parent's schedule is somewhat irregular throughout the day, an electric timer, the kind that can be set for hourly intervals, can be rigged up to ring a bell or buzzer whenever medication is due. A kitchen timer works as well, but it is a nuisance because it has to be reset after each use. There are even fancy electronic gadgets available. Regardless of the method you or your parents prefer, make sure that needed medications are not missed.

Summary

In contrast to some physicians, I encourage people to know as much about their health as possible. Unless the individual tries to second-guess the physician, information can do no harm. I do not recommend medical textbooks for this purpose, but I do recommend most of the books that have been written or edited by physicians but are directed to laypeople. Most large bookstores and libraries either have them or can get them. Certainly one should be in every home. Those with which I am familiar are listed at the end of this chapter.

You may be suspicious about my frequent references to your responsibility for the health of your parents who do not live near you. But do not be. Just a few days ago, a friend of ours telephoned her aging mother in another state. After a few moments, she said, "Mom, you don't sound right. Is anything wrong?" The mother replied, "You're right, dear. I don't feel well." The daughter told her mother to see her doctor, who discovered that she had congestive heart failure. Yes, I believe you can tell a lot about people from talking with them, even by phone, and even if they are trying to hide the truth. What they say, the way they say it, the vigor of their voice, the subjects they bring up, and the subjects they avoid all give signals to what is on their minds and how they feel. Learn to recognize these signals.

As I mentioned at the beginning of this chapter, there is no limit to the illnesses and the health hazards your parents may suffer. Your hope is that they will stay healthy. My hope is that you will know how to prevent that which is preventable and to handle those illnesses which they do contract with the skill of an understanding and loving middle-aged caregiver.

Miller, Benjamin F. *The Complete Medical Guide.* New York: Simon and Schuster, 1967.

Wagman, Richard J. and Sidney I. Landau. *The New Concise Family Health and Medical Guide.* Chicago: J. G. Ferguson Publishing Co., 1972.

Cooley, Donald G. (ed.). *After-40 Health and Medical Guide.* (Better Homes and Gardens Books). Des Moines, Iowa: Meredith Corporation, 1980.

Editors of Consumer Guide, *Family Medical Guide, The Illustrated Medical and Health Advisor.* Skokie, Ill.: Consumer Guide, 1983.

Kunz, Jeffery R. M. (ed). *AMA Family Medical Guide.* New York: Random House, 1982.

CHAPTER 11

The Drugs
They Take

Some drugs can do your parents great good. Others can do them great harm. If your parents cannot tell the difference because of any one of a number of reasons common to old age, it is your responsibility to help them determine which drugs are beneficial and which are harmful. There never has been, and probably never will be, a drug that is completely safe, one that will not cause some undesirable or even dangerous side effects, because most drugs are chemical substances quite foreign to the human body. Consequently, it is little wonder that some people at some time will have some trouble with some drugs.

Since every drug is formulated to affect the normal body chemistry in some predictable fashion, most Americans have come to believe that there is a curative drug for every symptom. True, there are many such drugs—drugs to put us to sleep and drugs to wake us up, drugs to dry our noses and drugs to moisten our coughs, drugs to stop pain and drugs to produce deep heat, drugs to tighten our bowels and drugs to open them up, drugs that help clot our blood and drugs that stop it from clotting, and for the young at heart drugs to increase fertility and drugs to inhibit it. You name it and, except for the magical waters from the fountain of youth, your corner pharmacy sells it.

Who buys these pretty packages? It is estimated that currently about 35 percent of the drugs manufactured and some one-fourth of the prescriptions written are used by people over sixty-five years of age, although they comprise only 12 percent of the population. So it is your aging parents who use many of them, and, consequently, it is your parents who will be either helped or harmed by them. You probably do not listen to the music of Lawrence Welk's orchestra on TV, but your parents do. Try that program sometime. You will not only hear some nice music, but you will learn what the drug manufacturers are trying to sell to your parents. One commercial after another is aimed at the expected infirmities of old age: arthritis, anemia, constipation, sore muscles, loose dentures, incontinence, insomnia, dry skin, and whatever else might befall the senior citizen. Advertisers certainly know their market.

Not all drugs are obtained over-the-counter from the corner pharmacy like those advertised on TV. Not by a long shot. Many, certainly the most powerful, are prescribed by physicians. In general, the more powerful the drug, the more likely the potential serious side effects, particularly in the elderly. These side effects can run from simple rashes to mental confusion—even to death. The literature describing a drug's potential side effects, called "adverse reactions" by the manufacturers, are listed not only in the advertisements physicians read but also in special leaflets called "package inserts." Most laymen do not see these information sheets, but any reputable physician or pharmacist will show them to you on request. Since they may list some fifty or so possible adverse reactions plus a number where the relationship to the drug has not yet been fully established, this information needs considerable professional interpretation for adequate understanding. Otherwise, it could scare your parents' pants off. Although many organizations such as the American Medical Association, the American Academy of Family Physicians, the U.S. Pharmacopeia, the American Society of Hospital Pharmacists, and others advocate that patients be provided with adequate drug information, a study done for the Food and Drug Administration showed that only 6 percent of patients received written consumer-oriented drug information from their physicians and only 15 percent from pharmacies. If your parents buy their drugs through the American Association of Retired Persons Pharmacy Service, they should receive such specially prepared, easy-to-understand information leaflets with each prescription.

The Food and Drug Administration has also prepared a helpful flier that has been widely distributed by the Social Security Administration, particularly to the elderly. It advises patients who are taking prescription medications to know:

- The name of the drug
- Its purpose
- How and when to take it
- When to stop
- What food, drinks, and other drugs to avoid while taking it
- What side effects may occur

It would be wise for your parents to heed these suggestions.

Since we seem to be a drug-oriented society, who is responsible for whatever excess drug usage we might find? Is it the patients, physicians, or pharmacists? Unfortunately, we see a lot of buck passing, but certainly all three are implicated. Every physician will tell you how often patients ask for, if not demand, a prescription. They appear to want a quick and easy solution to their problems. If the physician tries to dispense only advice or to promote a difficult and time-consuming behavior modification program for losing weight, exercising, or stopping smoking, the patient will seek another doctor, one who will give him or her a quick fix. Therefore, many physicians find it easier and quicker to prescribe drugs willy-nilly. Fortunately, most physicians are more thoughtful than that and will prescribe drugs only when there is a clear and safe indication. They well remember that Sir William Osler, the internationally famous patriarch of medicine, issued that specific warning over one hundred years ago. Pharmacists, although willing and able to give helpful advice on both over-the-counter and prescription medications, are more often treated as salesclerks than professionals. Not enough people ask enough questions.

Although I have implicated the physician and the pharmacist as the source of most drugs for your parents, they are, at least, knowledgeable. There is a third and surprisingly large group of well-intentioned but totally misinformed drug pushers. It includes one's friends, family, and on occasion complete strangers. Because these generous souls get relief from some medication, they foist it on everyone else who has the same symptoms. That is the worst kind of therapeutics. I not only caution you against joining that ghoulish group but also urge you to prevent your parents from getting sucked into the habit as well.

The media have a fondness for stories about new drugs and tout each one as a medical miracle. They tell how aspirin might slow the progression of cataracts or help in the prevention of second heart attacks, how vitamin A might help prevent cancer, how the industrial solvent DMSO might be useful for everything from muscle strains to chronic arthritis, or how large doses of vitamin C will abort the common cold. While there is a grain of truth in many of these newspaper stories, particularly those that have leaked out from reputable research laboratories, do not let your parents become guinea pigs or grabbers at straws. Regardless of their level of education, their economic status, or their trust in their physicians, the elderly will seek out and try anything and everything offering the slightest hope for relief or cure. Perhaps that is understandable. However, do not let your parents jump to false conclusions and begin self-treatment. Have them check with their doctor, who is just as anxious to use every new medical technique as anyone else. Their physician, however, will wait until he or she is sure each new drug is safe and effective. It is the quacks of this world who love older people, and they will sell them all sorts of gadgets, exotic diets, and magical potions offering cures for cancer, arthritis, and every other disease until our government properly puts them out of business. Do not let your parents make the quacks rich.

As drug takers, most people are not very sophisticated. They believe that if one pill will help, two will do better; that if a medication should be taken twice a day, three times would be more beneficial; and that if one type of medicine is helpful, a second one promising the same relief would guarantee the results. Incidentally, this is the same mentality we see in the youth of today, only in their case we call it "drug overdose."

Tactfully find out what drugs your parents are taking. Ask why they are taking them, and who prescribed them and when. Then try to determine if your parents are keeping to the proper schedules and dosages. This can be done by simple observation or by direct questioning. You may be well pleased with what you find out, because many older people are well able to handle their drugs by themselves. In those cases don't be a meddler. However, if they are on a medication and you or they observe no clinical improvement, it would be wise to butt in. They should consult their doctor again, because the dosage may need changing or even the drug itself. There is little value in taking a medication that is not doing any good. Of course, there are drugs like those for high blood pressure in which the therapeutic effect is not physically felt by the patient, but the value is enormous. However, even in these cases the physician should check on the patient periodically to be assured that the dosage and the drug selected are doing the job.

On the other hand, you might be amazed and chagrined at what you see and hear. I know I was when I had to help close my elderly uncle's small house after his death. From his medicine cabinet, linen closet, bathroom windowsill, kitchen counters, and sundry other places I collected enough medicine bottles, tubes, and containers to fill a thirty-two gallon trash can plus a bushel basket full to overflowing. Some of these preparations were so far outdated that, if taken, they would have proved either dangerous or ineffective. So I did what he should have done; I threw them out after first tossing the contents down the toilet so that no child or even an animal would think they were good to eat. If you ever find yourself in the same predicament, do the same thing.

Although this was a purely personal experience, do not be misled into thinking that it was an isolated incident. I heard of one case in which a patient was being treated by multiple physicians, none knowing what the other had ordered. As a result, the patient was taking nineteen different medications at various times throughout the day. Is it any wonder why such people lose their appetites and get worse rather than better?

If your parents are or ever have been in a nursing home, you will recognize the practice of putting each patient's medications in a shoebox or some similar container. This keeps each patient's drugs separate. I have had the displeasure of seeing some of these boxes and noting their contents. There is too often a mixture of prescription and over-the-counter drugs that would defy any thoughtful therapeutic plan for that patient. Can you imagine the chemical mishmash floating around in such a patient's blood and tissues? Because the normal metabolic processes that sustain life slow down in older people, drugs are not cleared or detoxified by their livers or excreted by their kidneys as fast as when they were younger. As a result, the drug levels in their bodies accumulate and toxicity replaces therapeutics.

If your parents are on such a merry-go-round, get them off. Talk to their doctor. Except for such specifics as insulin, antihypertensives, antibiotics which are bacteriologically indicated for limited periods, and a few other very special lifesaving drugs, more and more physicians are weaning their elderly patients away from such drug dependency. The results are often miraculous. Many patients clear mentally, regain their appetites, sleep better, their rashes disappear, and their whole outlook improves, all because drugs were stopped, not started.

However, for maximum results drugs should be replaced by an improved lifestyle. The elderly need exercise to stimulate their circulation and to keep their muscles in tone; they require a diet that responds to their nutritional and caloric needs; they require roughage for their bowels; and, not to be forgotten, they need stimulation for their minds. This is where you come in. If your parents are into drugs no less dangerously than the counterculture addicts of today, seek professional help. See to it that their drug intake is limited to those preparations that meet strict medical indications. Then get them started on a routine of healthy living.

By doing this, you will do your parents a double favor. You may not only save their lives, but you will save them a lot of money. The cost of drugs is enormous, and the cost of unnecessary and dangerous drugs is particularly tragic. Since many medications are for chronic diseases, these costs go on for years. Ask any older person how long he or she has been taking certain drugs. The length of time will surprise you. I have been taking an antihypertensive drug for over twelve years and plan to continue it for many more to come. However, dependency on pills for sleeping, weight reduction, nerves, constipation, gas, and various other minor and nonspecific complaints is no easier to break than it is to stop smoking, overeating, or drinking, but it is just as worthwhile. How much better it would be to have your parents spend their money on food, entertainment, and fun than on unnecessary, ineffective, or dangerous drugs.

Now that I have mentioned the high cost of drugs, let me add a word about generics. When a new drug is first developed, it is protected by a seventeen-year patent, which means the manufacturer sells it under its own brand name during that time. Once the patent has expired, any company, large or small, may make and sell the product under either a new brand name or under the drug's scientific or generic name. Consequently, generics should be just as good as brand-named products. However, variations may still occur. Although the active ingredients may be the same, the hardness, the uniformity of the dosage, the vehicle in which the drug is carried, and similar manufacturing processes may make a product act differently. Consequently, ask your parent's physician or pharmacist about the drug's clinical performance. That is the best criterion of all.

Where do placebos fit into a scientific therapeutic program? While placebos have no active ingredients, they do have a place in medicine. Unfortunately, we do not understand all the interactions between the mind and body, although we do know that such interactions do take place. For example, the brain can be stimulated to make its own pain-killing substances (endorphins) by faith and belief in the pain-killing powers of a placebo, thereby producing the desired results. So don't knock placebos. With the patient's belief and the doctor's psychological support, they can help and even do wonders. However, they should not be confused with ineffective nostrums which are sold on the pretext of containing secret and magical ingredients.

Since every coin has its reverse side, so does the taking of drugs. Whereas most people pop pills like candy, others will not let them cross their lips. I know of one elderly lady who boastfully pointed to a pile of unfilled prescriptions she had neatly placed in a pigeonhole in her desk. I am sure that her physician prided himself over the years with his therapeutic success in the care of this woman. Actually, by avoiding his prescribed drugs, she also avoided the rashes, upset stomachs, and other allergic disturbances she knew she would get if she took them. Unfortunately, her physician never asked her about such allergies before he wrote his prescriptions, and she found that it was better for her just to file them away. In deference to her intelligence, I must admit that she could discriminate when it was a matter of life or death. Those she had filled.

As you deal with your aging parents, be mindful of what drugs can and cannot do. Try to help them establish safe and sound drug habits. This means that they must take the proper dosage of the proper medicine at the proper hour for the proper length of time, and properly observe the warnings issued by the physician. These warnings might include instructions for taking the medicine with food, avoiding alcohol, or not driving. There is little use for an expensive prescription and then cancelling out its effectiveness by misusing it.

If you cannot get your point across, write to the Superintendent of Documents, U.S. Printing Office, Washington, DC 20402 for a booklet entitled "Using Your Medicines Wisely: A Guide for the Elderly." It offers sound, objective advice and might help you avoid a confrontation.

What should you know and do about the drugs or medications your parents are now taking? Please do not try to get the answers from some magazine or other publication—instead, ask your parent's physician or the pharmacist. Get the facts as they pertain to your parent's specific case, not to some theoretical average. Nevertheless, let me mention a few drugs you might be hesitant to ask about or you might not consider to be drugs.

Vitamin and Mineral Supplements

In any discussion of drugs, one cannot ignore vitamin and mineral supplements—although the subject more appropriately belongs under nutrition. However, since most people associate vitamins more with their medicine cabinets than with their refrigerators, I will include them here.

Vitamins are chemicals that are essential to life, as are a number of trace minerals which are often incorporated with vitamins in the same tablet or capsule. You might properly ask if it is really essential for your aging parents to take a vitamin and mineral supplement. Frankly, you will get an argument on that. Technically, if your parents consume an adequate diet, the answer is "probably no." Then, can they do your parents harm? The answer to that is "maybe but not likely," at least not at the dosages recommended on the package. However, vitamins in excessively high doses act as drugs, not dietary supplements, and can, as a result, cause the same undesirable side effects as any other drug. Specifically, if abnormal amounts of the fat-soluble vitamins A and D, but apparently not E or K, accumulate in the body tissues, minor problems can arise. Of these, vitamin D is perhaps the most toxic because large amounts can lead to calcification of soft tissue. Recently, overdoses of vitamin B6 have been reported to cause certain neurological symptoms.

With the exception of iron, which if taken in large doses can do damage, the amounts of essential minerals in these preparations are sufficiently small so as not to present any threat. But treat all vitamins and mineral supplements with respect. Be cautious. Don't let your parents, searching for a miracle, treat them like candy.

But with all of this hemming and hawing, should or should not multiple vitamin and mineral supplements be used by elderly individuals? Are they of any value? As I indicated earlier, some think "yes," others "no." Personally I do not hesitate to recommend them, provided they are taken in accordance with the instructions on the package. Many elderly, some nonmeat eaters (but not true vegetarians), alcoholics, those on reducing diets, and the economically disadvantaged usually have diets less than adequate in the essentials. For them, the indication is clear. Yes, take supplemental vitamins and minerals by all means. For those whose diets are adequate or at least marginal, the need thins out. The catch comes when there is a difference in the amount of vitamins swallowed and the amount absorbed into the system. Many elderly do not have the same ability to absorb nutrients from their digestive tracts as they did in their younger years. Therefore, a balanced diet may not necessarily provide enough vitamins and minerals. Adding some may make up for your aging parent's poor absorption. Certainly, an inadequate intake of vitamins is a greater threat to health than vitamin toxicity, because all but two vitamins are found in food. Some vitamin D comes from the action of the sun on exposed skin, and about half of vitamin K is produced by normal bacteria in the intestinal tract. Your parents have to eat the rest.

Except in those few and rare cases of proven avitaminosis, the addition of vitamins will create little dramatic therapeutic effect. They will not enhance one's verve, vitality, or virility. There are some early claims that vitamin C may help prevent stomach cancer and that beta-carotene, a natural form of vitamin A found in yellow and dark green vegetables, might help in preventing bacteria in the bowel from forming cancer-causing substances. Some people claim a sense of improved well-being, but that is hard to evaluate or to quantify. So the last word on vitamins is not in yet. If your parents think a multiple vitamin and mineral supplement helps, give them the benefit of the doubt. Who cares? In the doses recommended they will do no harm, may do some good, and if they are unneeded, will pass out of the body unnoticed.

Sleeping Pills

Whether prescribed by physicians or purchased over the counter for self-medication, sleeping pills are big business. There is a wide variety of these drugs, and most are excellent for acute bouts of insomnia such as might occur during family and personal crises. However, most people who buy sleeping pills do so because of chronic difficulty in either getting to sleep or staying asleep, not because of acute crises. Believe it or not, the chronic use of sleeping pills can itself cause insomnia, particularly in the elderly. If your parents complain of insomnia and take sleeping pills every night, often in increasing dosages, stop the drug. Normal sleep patterns should return in due time. Substitute normal sleep-producing methods such as warm milk, avoidance of naps, no drinks containing caffeine, no stimulating activity prior to retiring, daily exercise, comfortable room temperature, and even weight reduction if the patient is obese. Sleep patterns differ. Some sleep disturbances are severe enough to require a more careful work-up, but for now, if your parents are taking sleeping pills and are still not sleeping, stop the pills.

Alcohol

Although few think of alcohol as a drug, it is one of the oldest, most powerful, most useful, most dangerous, and most frequently used drugs we have today. While it is used in the manufacture of many preparations, its main use and abuse is as a social beverage.

If one or more of your parents were heavy drinkers, chances are they have long since passed away. Statistics show that the mortality rate of those consuming six or more drinks per day over prolonged periods is double that of the total abstainer. Your concern, therefore, is how the drinking habits of your living parents will affect them—and you. If they have been moderate to heavy drinkers, the alcohol has probably already done some damage to their livers, brains, and nervous systems, and has increased their chances of cirrhosis as well as cancer of the liver, mouth, and esophagus, and perhaps even of the lung, pancreas, intestines, and prostate. If they are both heavy drinkers and heavy smokers, chances are they will suffer from breathing problems as well. In comparison to nondrinkers, they will certainly have more frequent hospitalizations, a greater risk of accidents and suicide, increased social problems, a deteriorating memory, and a

growing personal dependence. These problems may also lead to economic hardships, particularly for those with modest means. No, it is
not a bright picture.

Consequently, you might properly ask how much alcohol is safe?
The answer is not as simple as Carry Nation, the early temperance
leader, believed. Recent studies have shown that one or even two
small drinks per day might actually be good for one's heart. However,
nearly twenty million of our fellow citizens have some still unknown
genetic or biologic defect that causes them special problems in handling alcohol. For them, any alcohol is too much. Total abstinence is
their only way to avoid the horrors of chronic alcoholism.

All of this leaves you with few choices. If your parents are heavy
drinkers, plan to have more problems with them than most other people with their aging parents. Obviously, try to restrict their intake of
alcohol. Seek help from their physician or from an agency that deals
with alcoholism. Such agencies are usually listed in the phone book
and are known to health professionals, social workers, and the clergy.
I can assure you that we have seen failures as well as successes, but the
quest is worth the try. Since every bit of alcohol adds to the damage,
every bit of abstinence not only prevents further damage but also gives
nature a little better chance of healing the damage already done.

If one of your parents is scheduled for surgery, be sure to advise
the surgeon of his or her alcohol habit. Do not be embarrassed. Delirium tremens is a rather nasty complication that can occur in a chronic
alcoholic who is suddenly deprived of alcohol in any postoperative period. However, if forewarned, it can be prevented and adequately
handled with available drugs.

Blessed are you if your parents are light drinkers—that is, if they
consume not more than one drink per day. If they can stay at that
level and not become heavy drinkers, let them be. They will be better
off because of the protective effects on their hearts that small doses of
alcohol seem to give.

Also sit tight for those who are now total abstainers, and for
heaven's sake, don't get them started. You can never tell ahead of
time if they are among that small percentage who cannot tolerate alcohol and who, if started, would quickly become chronic alcoholics.

In dealing with your elderly parents, watch your own behavior.
Do not make it difficult for them to maintain a healthy lifestyle. Protect them from their well-intentioned but poorly informed friends who
in the spirit of hospitality thrust upon them the alcohol they should
not have.

Caffeine

Caffeine is a chemical found in certain plants and produced in the laboratory in vast quantities. The fact that it is found in coffee, tea, and colas as well as in many prescription and over-the-counter preparations makes it eligible, as are vitamins, to be discussed either under drugs or under nutrition. Since the chemical itself has no intrinsic food value, perhaps it is best discussed as a drug.

Most people know that caffeine increases the output of urine, and they plan their daily activities around that fact. Many also recognize its stimulating effect on the central nervous system—causing everything from mild irritability to severe insomnia, depending on the individual's own sensitivity. Caffeine is also a circulatory stimulant and can cause a mild increase in blood pressure as well as disturbances in the rhythm of the heartbeat. Because of its stimulating effects, caffeine has a number of medicinal purposes. However, since most elderly do not need such stimulation, try to help them avoid caffeine as much as possible.

If you notice that your elderly parents are drinking coffee frequently and are complaining of insomnia, nervousness, or frequent urination, don't panic. Have them try to give up coffee or, at least, switch to decaffeinated brands. Reducing one's intake of caffeine after years of indulgence may cause minor headaches, but they are usually temporary. If your parents' only indiscretion is one or two cups of coffee a day, and they show no ill effects, don't worry. But remember, to this daily allowance do not add tea or colas. As with alcohol, do not push caffeine-containing beverages onto your parents and do not let their friends do it either. There are an increasing number of satisfying beverages that are now caffeine-free. Read the labels; they should let you know. Remember, caffeine will never help your parents grow old gracefully.

Nicotine

Perhaps you or your parents never associated tobacco smoking and the taking of drugs, but if you have not, you are mistaken. According to the dictionary, nicotine is a "poisonous alkaloid derived from the tobacco plant, used in medicine and as an insecticide." Its current use as a medicine is nil and as an insecticide not much better. So if your parents come in contact with it at all, it will be through the smoking of tobacco. Although the nicotine content of most modern filter cigarettes is somewhat reduced, it is not totally eliminated. Furthermore, nicotine is not the only culprit in smoke. Cigarettes also contain tars and carbon monoxide, neither of which promotes health. Carbon monoxide, as you may know, decreases the capacity of red blood cells to carry needed oxygen to the body's tissues. In addition, there are dozens, maybe hundreds, of chemicals used as additives in the manufacture of various cigarettes whose effects on throat, lung, and other tissues are essentially unknown. Certainly, there is no totally safe cigarette. Pipe and cigar smoking have their own problems, but except for cancer of the lip in chronic pipe smokers, they have been linked with systemic disease less dramatically than cigarettes because less smoke is inhaled.

Therefore, what efforts should you take if your parents smoke tobacco? If their physician suggests that they stop because of some specific health reason such as heart disease or emphysema, by all means help them stop. Although nicotine appears addictive, some individuals can give up the habit cold turkey, while others must taper off. Some are not able to give it up at all, but they must try.

Once lung cancer is diagnosed, it is too late to worry about preventing disease but not too late to worry about the adverse effects smoking will have on one's few remaining months. Early, precancerous damage to lung tissues caused by smoking can be reversed by discontinuing the thermal and chemical onslaught. So if your parents want to protect themselves as much as is humanly possible, suggest that they give up smoking. If they are suffering from some rapidly progressive terminal illness not harmed by smoking and they enjoy a puff or two, let them smoke. That gesture is like giving a cigarette to a condemned man before a firing squad. You are no longer worried about preventing disease.

Marijuana

Marijuana (*cannabis*) is a powerful drug. It is not something to be toyed with. A report published by the Addiction Research Foundation of Ontario, Canada, and the World Health Organization covering the work of twenty-eight of the world's leading researchers in ten countries concluded that marijuana causes "a broad range of risks to health." The report noted that the elderly may be more sensitive to its effects because, as I mentioned earlier, drugs are not cleared or detoxified as fast in the elderly as they are in younger people. While it is true that marijuana is being used in some cases to reduce the side effects of cancer therapy, this is a decision for an experienced physician. Don't assume that you can do your aging parents a favor by slipping them a marijuana cigarette. You can't.

Drug Wrap-Up

In addition to these few specific drugs or chemicals that people intentionally come in contact with, the world is full of other substances that are potentially dangerous to their health, many of which are environmental pollutants. If your parents were exposed to any known dangerous chemical or substance on their jobs or in their hobbies, their physician should be notified. He or she might have some specific helpful advice.

As I said at the beginning of this chapter, drugs have the potential of doing good or of doing harm. Your aging parents will likely use drugs more heavily than any other member of your family, so make sure that they use them as wisely, as effectively, and as inexpensively as possible.

CHAPTER 12

They Are
What They Eat

*I*f for any reason your parents were denied a minimally basic diet after you were born or, at the other extreme, indulged themselves in unmitigated gluttony, chances are they are no longer living. Hopefully your aging parents have been more fortunate or prudent in their eating habits. If so, your present concern will be to see that nothing interferes with that happy equilibrium. Yet in our complex society eating serves more than a nutritional function. It has many social, medical, emotional, economic, religious, and ethnic ramifications.

Next to fashions in dress, and more recently in sexual mores, there are more fads involving nutrition than in any other facet of our daily lives. However, it is unusual for the elderly to fall for such gimmicks. They have accepted their bodies as they are. They have no statements to make and little or no peer pressure to worry about. In fact, few could reach a perfect ten even if they bribed the judges. This does not mean to say that the elderly do not care about their appearance. They do. They just do not go overboard for fads. Those who do enjoy lean, trim, and fashionable figures as senior citizens were probably that way for many years before they turned sixty-five. They were the fortunate ones who lucked into the right combination of good genes, proper eating habits, healthful exercise, and, yes, good teeth. Much of good nutrition depends on the ability to chew properly. Painful or missing teeth or bad fitting dentures hinder nutrition. You will certainly know if your parents suffer from such annoying problems by direct observation or from the crescendo of repeated complaints. Your parents' doctor should have warned them of this and chased them to a dentist. If their physician has not, why don't you do the chasing? A generation ago most elderly had dentures or gummed their way through old age. Now, we are expected to keep our natural teeth throughout our whole lives, but it takes considerable effort on the part of each individual and his or her dentist to save them.

Eating habits generally start in early childhood. To understand why your parents eat the way they do, you have to understand the forces that shaped their lives sixty to seventy years ago. That was a different age. Food-wise, it was a more simple and natural time. If their cultural roots stressed body fat either as a sign of affluence or as a protection against the cold, or if their mothers pushed food as charter members of the Clean Plate Club, they probably are on the plump side today. Similarly, if their mothers cooked fatty or lean, spicy or bland, traditional or ethnic foods, they probably prefer those same kinds of food even today. What is more, your mother probably fed those foods to you when you were growing up. However, many people abandon these traditions over the years as they intermingle and intermarry with people of different dietary backgrounds. You or your parents may be such mavericks.

For the healthy person up in years, I offer few dietary rules. I will approve of just about anything anyone enjoys eating provided it is not harmful to their health and contains the basic elements of good nutrition. When one learns of the strange things different people around the world eat and thrive on, it would be foolish for me to tell anyone what to put into his or her mouth. While it is said that people are what they eat, it is true only in respect to the nutritional building blocks in their diets, not in the way it smells, tastes, or looks on the plate. However, the purpose of this chapter is not to teach nutrition or the elements of a balanced diet, nor is its purpose to describe specific diets or to supply caloric values of specific foods. Those facts are adequately taught either in the grade schools or in books on nutrition. Rather, its purpose is to remind you how food relates to the health and happiness of your aging parents.

Economics, both family and national, greatly influence eating habits. Diets inadequate in protein and calories will lead to emaciation in direct proportion to the degree of starvation. We see this in pictures of undernourished children and adults in economically depressed countries. However, even the poor in our own nation often find it difficult to buy the meats and fish, bread and cereals, fruits and vegetables, and dairy products necessary to provide a balanced diet. As a consequence, they resort to less expensive foods high in fat, starch, and sugars which, although increasing body weight, can also spell malnutrition. Therefore, do not evaluate your parents' nutritional status from the sex, height, and weight tables alone. Look at what they eat.

Good nutrition, at least in that segment of our urban population denied the opportunity for home gardens, depends on good shopping habits. Financial resources have a lot to do with one's ability to purchase good nutrition, but not entirely. When I shop or accompany my wife, I shudder at what appears to be the typical market basket of some senior citizens. Many tend to buy expensive cuts of meats with heavy marbling of fat or go to the other extreme and purchase tasty convenience foods with high fat content, fillers, and additives. Many stock up on a disproportionate amount of sweets and bakery goods high in refined sugars, and they hide on the bottom of the cart bottled drinks high in caffeine. They are impulsive buyers, purchasing what looks good at the moment.

On the other hand, I have noticed an equal number of elderly, particularly couples, who are very prudent buyers. They plan a menu and shop accordingly. They buy foods with nutritional value, yet take advantage of sales and coupons as all shoppers should. It would appear that many of these wise shoppers are making things from scratch: breads, stews, soups, casseroles, salads, and other nutritious dishes. Good for them! Extra credit should go to those who freeze or can foods when they are plentiful and inexpensive. By so doing, they will be able to avoid the salt, sugar, and preservatives added to many commercial products.

I cannot speak for all areas of the country, but many chain stores offer discounts to senior citizens, primarily in the hope of attracting more customers on their slow days. Your parents, regardless of income, should plan their shopping to take advantage of these discounts. Why not? That means they can eat better for the same money.

Yes, I think it would be wise if you checked into your parents' shopping practices. Peek into their refrigerators and cupboards if you have any doubts. You may learn something, but again, you may not. Don't waste your time if you are reassured from what they serve or from the way they look and act, but if you suspect that there might be an economic, emotional, or medical problem interfering with their nutrition, a quick look-see might give you a lead. Some proud older people are hesitant to seek help from either family or outside agencies, and as a result might try to solve their financial problems by stinting on food. They may suffer some unexplained stomach problem after eating which causes them to restrict their intake. Whatever the reason, catch it early before malnutrition lowers their resistance to other health problems. If you and your brothers and sisters live so far away from your parents that you do not see them frequently, ask about their nutrition when you phone or write. You ask about everything else— why not slip in an innocuous question about nutrition? If there is a problem, their answer might give you an important clue.

What people buy also depends in large measure upon their skill in cooking. I never really appreciated the difference that skill made until World War II. I thought that all Army food was the same because it all came from the same warehouse. However, two groups changed my mind. The first were Army cooks who had previously been Pullman dining car chefs and the second were Italian prisoners-of-war who had cooked professionally before the war. Both were able to turn basic Army foodstuffs into meals far more attractive and tasty than those found in most mess halls.

Many senior centers and health departments offer periodic instruction by trained dieticians to assist the elderly in buying and preparing economical but attractive and nutritious meals. They would be flattered to have your parents as students. No, your parents are not too old to learn some new tricks.

If your mother was a good cook in her younger years, and if she had a large family to feed on a limited budget, she can be excused from scrutiny because she has the skills to do well in her golden years. I worry more about your father if he is a widower and never had the responsibility for planning or preparing meals. I have known two elderly gentlemen both retired on modest but adequate incomes, who took two completely different paths when confronted with this situation. One took a cooking course designed for elderly individuals living alone. The shopping forced him out of the house, breaking up the monotony of the day, and his cooking broke up the boredom at home. He became a very creative cook and enjoyed good nutrition. The other, a bachelor, had been a traveling salesman and had few domestic skills. Once when I was visiting him in his small apartment I noticed a stack at least five feet high of empty, but fortunately washed, aluminum TV dinner trays. Apparently, he was saving them for an aluminum recycling drive, but can you imagine how many lonely TV dinners he must have eaten? I do not want to discount the nutritional value of frozen dinners or their convenience and quality, because they serve many useful purposes. But for the same money and with a little skill this old gentleman could have had better nutrition, more variety, and greater enjoyment. Yet I admit cooking for one is no easy or pleasant task; however, there are a number of good cookbooks to help out in this lonely endeavor. A few foods, such as soups and canned goods, are now prepared for single servings, but the price per portion is not favorable.

Eating alone is not the most stimulating activity I can think of, and your parents will attest to that. In fact, it is understandably difficult for individuals living alone to thoroughly enjoy their meals or to achieve good nutrition. It is no better for those who are depressed, ill, or insecure for any of a dozen reasons. But even if both of your parents are still living, there will be times when the one who does most of the shopping and cooking may be in the hospital or nursing home or out of the house because of some happy or sad occasion, forcing the other to eat alone. Even an illness of one partner within the home may force the other to eat alone or, heaven forbid, to place the noncooking partner in charge of feeding the other.

The Meals-on-Wheels program or its equivalent around the country is a godsend in such situations. The availability of one well-prepared hot meal, if augmented by a light breakfast and supper, is enough to supply a day's nutrition. Should your parents have difficulty in cooking for themselves, you might try to find such a resource. Unfortunately, most such programs do not operate on weekends. Unless you either provide the same service or invite them to your place, the weekends will become pretty hungry times for your parents. If more than one sibling is in the neighborhood—which is frequently the case—share the responsibility.

On weekdays, in contrast to the typical family where the breadwinner is at work and the children are in school at noon, the elderly often eat their main meal at midday, not at the end of the workday. This has many advantages for them, but it must be reckoned with whenever your activities impinge upon theirs.

In addition to the services where meals are delivered to the elderly in their homes, there are many nutrition centers sponsored by churches or other agencies to which the elderly may go regardless of income. These offer many advantages of companionship and the ability to match portions with appetites, but, of course, they have the disadvantage of having to go outdoors often in bad weather. Some elderly living alone have joined up with a few neighbors and friends to eat together in round-robin fashion. This type of cooperative eating not only relieves the loneliness and the necessity to cook every day, but it offers an intimacy not found in community dining halls, greater variety, often less distances to travel, and some savings in cost over eating at home. However, an enduring compatibility of the participants is the key to the success of such joint ventures.

Appetite is a fickle sensation easily lost. Conversely, effective appetizers are few and far between, the best being attractive and tasty foods that give off delicious aromas during preparation and that are consumed in a relaxed atmosphere with pleasant company. If you can help your aging parents approximate that atmosphere, go to it! Urge them to participate in one of the alternative eating arrangements, perhaps on a part-time basis if that suits their needs best. They may not have thought of such opportunities.

I have been amazed at the number of senior citizens who dine out, particularly those in urban areas. Those of modest means often frequent the fast-food places at times when the younger, more boisterous crowds are not there. The more affluent eat in more conventional restaurants. Here again, your parents should seek out eating establishments which give discounts to senior citizens. Furthermore, as most older people know, the same meal often costs less at noon than at night. Do not let your parents offer any feeble excuses for not being able to stick to their diets at restaurants. A vegetable plate can always be arranged and will substitute admirably for most diets. If they are on a low salt or no butter regimen, suggest that your parents ask that no salt or butter be used in the preparation of their entrée. This is quite feasible for most cooked-to-order items. Have them ask for margarine instead of butter, for decaffeinated coffee, and to have their meats chopped if that is necessary. Most restaurants are happy to cater to the elderly, but a little extra tip might make it easier the next time. Airlines are equally cooperative if advised prior to departure, and they will not expect a tip.

Senior citizens love to eat. You must have guessed that by now. If you put two or more of them together, regardless of their weights, within two minutes they will be talking about food or about some new eating experience. Imperceptibly, within the next two minutes the conversation will become a confessional. Each will tell about breaking his or her diet the day before. "It looked so good," they will confess, "I just couldn't resist. I'm sure a little bit couldn't hurt. Don't you agree?" Your parents are probably no different. I remember meeting one bright gentleman at a senior citizens' center who remarked that attendance was always better when food was served. He was right. Senior citizens do much of their socializing around food. Every meeting requires cake and coffee. So keep up the tradition. Diets need not be designed to take the fun out of eating. Both nutrition and pleasure can be accommodated. Invite your parents to your house or take them out to a restaurant. They'll love it. What am I saying? You probably do that already so please forgive me for butting in.

Many elderly put themselves on a diet because of vanity or because they have heard that it is the healthy thing to do. Selecting such a self-imposed diet is something like buying furniture. It has to fit one's individual needs and budget; it has to be practical; it has to be satisfactory to those who might share it; and it must be something the individual can enjoy for a long time. Again, like furniture, many people can create a tasteful, comfortable room by using their own common sense. Others, who have very unusual situations or lack the basic skills of interior design, must rely on the help of outside decorators. Similarly, some can devise healthy and satisfying diets. Those who have a more difficult problem or who lack the fundamental understanding of nutrition must seek the advice of a professional.

If your parents are in this latter group and are on a strict diet imposed by medical necessity, it would be wise to keep your eyes and ears open. Although most elderly are good patients, it takes an understanding doctor with an exceptional ability to communicate to make an older person conform to the rigors of a strict diet. It may even take more than gentle persuasion. It may take a threat or a scare to force them to change those practices which in their eyes have worked so well in the past. If both of your parents can go on the same diet at the same time, it will be easier all around. People on diets need a lot of support. So help them, encourage them, compliment them. But by all means, don't tempt them. Don't eat a sticky, frosted pecan bun while they are nibbling on a piece of dry toast.

As I said earlier, I am not going to prescribe any diets. I will leave that to your parents' own physician. He or she is the one to determine the do's and don'ts. This may be done in the office, or through referral of your mother or father to a trained dietician who can carry out the physician's broad instructions by helping with menu planning, food buying, portion control, preparation, and serving. What the physician and dietician cannot do is continuously monitor your parents' compliance by personal observation unless, of course, your parents are confined to some sort of a custodial institution. Otherwise, these professionals have to depend on what they see and hear. Yet we know that those on diets often bend the truth. If the therapeutic results and the patient's story do not match, the truth has probably been twisted. If you and your parents make up an extended family, you can easily influence their compliance. But the greater the distance separating you and your parents, the less likely you can monitor their performance. However, by asking "How's the diet going, Mom?" you will put her on notice that you think her diet is important to her continued good health. As I said, people on diets need reinforcement. Give it to them! Whatever you do, don't help them break their diets. If your custom has been to give a box of candy to your diabetic mother or a three-foot link of gift sausage to your hypertensive father for their anniversary or some other gift-giving occasion, stop it. Become more creative! Maybe, you will have to go back to flowers and neckties, but if they do not appeal, try fruit. Most parents will love it, and it will be good for them.

One of the best ways to help your parents stay on a diet, particularly a weight-control diet, is to have them talk to someone who has been successful at it. A favorable report of feeling better physically and having a better self-image emotionally will be strong reinforcement. If outside help is needed to obtain permanent behavior modification, there are such places in most larger communities willing to take on the job for a few dollars. Being a cheapskate, I find that the price of a new suit is enough motivation to keep me from gaining weight.

As you would expect, the diet most frequently imposed on the elderly is for overweight, or obesity, although few individuals including physicians could adequately define the term. In spite of this, we glibly say that over one-third of all people are overweight, and a good share of these are over the age of sixty-five. We know that some people are built differently than others and that diet alone will not alter their basic makeup. We get our best information about the relationship between health status and weight from the National Institute on Aging. In general, their statistics do not confirm the popular belief that skinny people live longer than fat people. Rather they suggest that both the very lean and the very fat have the highest death rates. However, weight alone is less important in determining mortality than such factors as hypertension, smoking, inactivity, etc. Nevertheless, you should not completely ignore weight when you contemplate your parents' health. You may recall that my second commandment for long life in Chapter 10 suggested that in respect to weight one should stay "close to the norms." Therefore, make a healthy weight for your parents a goal but not a fetish.

We all know from the public media that excess weight imposes an undue strain on the heart, blood vessels, and joints, as well as predisposing to diabetes, gall bladder disease, and other medical complications. Most surgeons and anesthetists can tell you the handicap that an overweight patient suffers when undergoing surgery. There is some early statistical evidence that women who are 40 percent or more overweight might have higher rates of cancer of the breast, uterus, and ovaries, and that overweight men might have a higher risk of cancer of the colon, prostate, and rectum. I'm sure you could tell me about your skinny neighbor who had one of these cancers or about your rotund butcher who didn't. I did not say that if your parents were fat, they would get cancer or that if they were skinny, they would not. I merely said that, in certain statistical studies, that's what the facts prove. Consequently, if I had my way, I would prefer that my parents stayed close to the norms.

From your own observation you must know the toll that obesity takes. Match a cross section of the general population with a group of senior citizens. You will notice that the variations in weight are less extreme in the elderly. There are fewer very skinny and fewer very fat people. To put it bluntly, that observation confirms the national statistics that the very thin and the very heavy either corrected their problem or are no longer living.

As I look back at my own experience with weight gain and at those around me, I am convinced, although completely unconfirmed by science, that there must be within us some sort of weight regulator. When we get to be about forty-five, it tells our slim, sleek bodies that the youthful days of summer are over, and like the grizzly bear we should accumulate fat to prepare for the long, halcyon days of old age. Whether or not that is true does not matter. Your parents will use the same shabby rationalization to argue that they cannot control their weight, so why go on any silly diet at their age. Apropos of this, have you ever heard older people say that if they had to change doctors, they would find a portly one, not some skinny kid who wants to rid the world of fat?

The relationship of obesity, fatty foods, and salt to hypertension and other cardiovascular diseases is now household knowledge. I would bet that your parents are aware of these relationships and that they may well be doing something about it even without specific medical advice. I hope they are. Incidentally, do your parents still have a salt shaker on the table? If so, hide it. Does your mother still keep a big container of salt near the stove? If so, plug some of the holes. Stress the danger of too much salt. My wife and I have limited our salt intake for years, so much so that most restaurant meals now taste unpleasantly salty. Not everyone, however, is equally harmed by salt. The trouble is that you will never know how your parents will react to excess salt until the damage is done. So, say goodbye to salt.

Do not let your parents get hung up on cholesterol, triglycerides, high-density lipoproteins, polyunsaturated fats, etc. Let their doctor worry about those, and have an appropriate diet be prescribed if necessary. Sure, you can stress that they cut down on red meats and dairy fats and substitute fish, chicken, and turkey (without the skin and fat). You can also emphasize that fatty foods should be used in considerable moderation but not avoided altogether. Your parents could not avoid fat in their diet if they wanted to, unless they went on intravenous feedings. A diet without fat would be unbalanced. In fact, if you do not get enough, your body will make some.

Fiber is another popular word these days, but do not be fooled into thinking that manufacturers are adding it. They just aren't taking it out. Dietary fiber is a natural product. It is in unprocessed grains and seeds, nuts, the skins of fruit and berries, root vegetables, and many other garden grown foods. Bran, the outer husks of grain removed during processing, is used alone or added to many food items to increase dietary fiber.

Although many claims and counterclaims have been made linking inadequate dietary fiber and roughage to bowel cancer and diverticulosis, fiber has its greatest use in the relief of simple constipation. Whereas a group of active senior citizens might talk about food, the nursing-home set talks about constipation. If either subject comes up in conversations with your parents, at least you will have some answers for both.

We tend to ignore water or other fluids when we speak of nutrition. That is a great mistake. Water is necessary even if one is on diuretics. It is what we add to water—such as sugar, flavorings, caffeine, and chocolate—that upsets the balance of many diets. Milk, particularly skim milk, supplies not only fluid but also calcium needed for healthy bone generation.

There are many other diets that may be prescribed for your parents such as those for diabetes, hypertension, arthritis, allergies, gall bladder disease, diverticulitis, anemias, some ulcers, gout, and so on. Most of these will be designed either to add or to subtract some specific substance from your parents' daily intake. This means that the diet has a specific medical indication and should be carefully observed. The day of the shotgun method of prescribing diets from hearsay evidence is gone. That reminds me of the lady who asked her physician if he was going to prescribe a diet for her. He said, "No, eat anything you wish, but come to think of it, stay away from curried shrimp." When asked why he made such an unusual recommendation, he offered, "I had some last night, and it damned near killed me."

Your parents will be better off if they eat properly and stay on whatever diet may have been prescribed by their doctor. Their ability to maintain adequate nutrition or to follow a medically necessary regimen may be one of the more pivotal factors in determining if they can continue to be safe and healthy in their own home. If they cannot maintain adequate nutrition, if a substitute or supplemental food source is not available, or if it does not meet their specific needs, thought must be given to an alternative care system outside of the home. That means that because they cannot eat properly, they have to give up their own home, spend more money for their daily care, move away from friends, and lose the last vestige of freedom and independence. Not a pleasant outcome from such a simple thing as not being able to eat properly. Therefore, to prevent this tragedy befalling your parents, watch their nutrition. There may come a time when they cannot make it on their own, but do not let it be from poor nutrition. In great measure such problems are preventable either by your parents or by you and your family.

CHAPTER 13

Homes Away
from Home

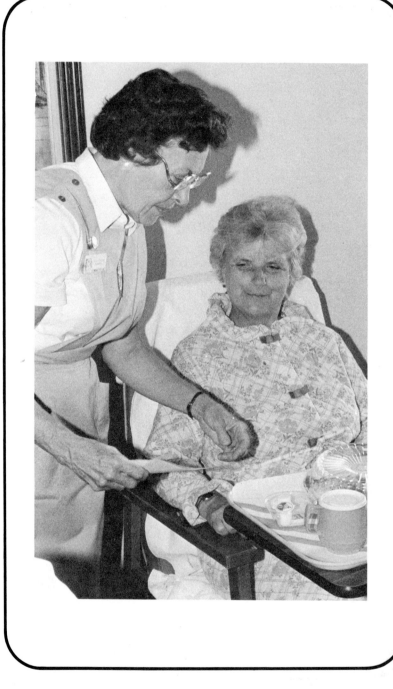

Photo by Virginia Kraucunas

*T*o your aging parents, there is no place like home. They will resist leaving it with the tenacity of a mad bulldog. Whether their home is a castle or a hovel, their reaction will be the same—"I'm staying!" As we have seen in Chapter 6, "Home Sweet Home," this could be a rational decision, provided that your parents are physically and mentally able to care for themselves. It might also be rational if they share their homestead with an adult son or daughter, with some other relative, or even with a friend willing and able to provide the attention they need both day and night. Of course, if they are taken seriously ill or suffer an accident requiring hospitalization, they may accept a temporary dislocation—but even then only reluctantly and tearfully.

Facts of life being what they are, there might well come a time when it will not be possible for your mother and father to stay in their own home. Paid or volunteer health aides and homemakers may permit them to enjoy their home a little longer than might otherwise be expected, but eventually that support system will break down. Infirmities such as blindness, the inability to get out of bed unaided, the need for special nursing care and dozens of other medical or social problems can precipitate the unwelcomed decision to leave home.

Have you ever discussed this possibility with your parents? Whether or not you have, it looms on the horizon. So be prepared by having a few thoughts pulled together. Open up a dialogue at some appropriate time and find out what your parents might want. Discuss it with other members of your family. Moving your mother and father will be a lot more successful and a lot less nerve-wracking if both of you plan ahead.

Like it or not, at some time in their later years your parents, alone or together, may be compelled to move either on a temporary or permanent basis into one or more of the following "homes away from home":

I. Home of a Relative or Friend

II. Hospital

    1. Acute general hospital
    2. Ambulatory or day surgery
    3. Psychiatric hospital

4. Rehabilitation hospital
5. Day hospital

III. Nursing Home

IV. Hospice

Home of a Relative or Friend

The most frequent move by far is to the home of a relative—usually a son or daughter, occasionally a brother or sister, and rarely a more distant relative. Once in a great while an aging individual moves in with a friend often of about the same age and usually of the same sex, but the success of this arrangement depends on the health of the second individual. This latter solution may not only be temporary, but it also may complicate the care of your aging parent. Trouble may be doubled.

Many of the elderly resist moving in with one of their sons or daughters even more violently than they resist leaving home in the first place. They just don't want to be a burden, and would prefer almost any other alternative solution. Of course, in many rural sections of our country and in many ethnic neighborhoods moving in with the children is the traditional way of caring for the elderly. In these cases the move may be distressing but not disastrous. Since it is expected at some time, it merely represents the unfolding of a predetermined plan.

However, in no case is the move easy. It usually means giving up a roomy, old home full of furniture and memories for a small bedroom from which the occupant, probably a school-age child, has been banished. It will be even more difficult if your parents have been sleeping in separate rooms by reason of choice or necessity. Remember that snoring, disturbed sleep patterns, or the need to void one or more times each night, while not destroying a marriage, can destroy the fun of sleeping together. When your parents do have to break up their home, few of their belongings can be moved except for some minor personal items and mementos. Since the sale or disposition of their cherished possessions would be so painful to your parents, it would be best if you could discuss the principles of the disposal with them, but handle the details yourself. Depending on the quality or suitability of certain pieces, there might be some swapping—their good sofa for your bad one or their fine set of china and silverware for your chipped and twisted stuff. Young newlyweds, college students, or friends of the family might find use for some pieces and at the same time give your parents some pleasure by knowing that their treasures made someone else happy. A garage sale might get rid of some items, but do not expect to dispose of an entire household by that method. Charitable organizations will gladly accept usable items and give your parents a tax deduction to boot. However, do not try to pawn off broken-down, overstuffed furniture or good-for-nothing appliances to charities, because they don't want them. Libraries may accept used books in good condition, but do not be surprised if they sell or give away most of them after selecting those which might be added to their collection. Museum-quality artifacts are not very plentiful, but if something is truly old or rare, a museum might be interested. Although your folks may have spent a small fortune over the years in furnishing their home, do not let them expect too much in return—even if the disposition is through an estate sale or auction. Antique dealers might show a momentary interest, hoping to find some undiscovered treasure, but do not count on it. At best, you will do a lot of work for a very slim financial return.

If the house is some distance away, if the timetable for its disposition is tight, or if other matters take priority, you and your parents might have to move the stuff temporarily and place it in local storage. This is an expensive and awkward alternative that should be avoided if possible.

Unless the house is rented or already committed to someone else, it will have to be sold, which is not an easy task unless the property is particularly desirable. The proceeds from the sale, however, will permit your parents to augment whatever other savings they might have. This, in turn, will give them enough resources to help them contribute to the expenses of their new home, whatever and wherever it may be.

Understandably, but quite regrettably, the care of aging parents under these deteriorating circumstances usually falls to a daughter of the family. If perchance she is unmarried, she is elected by acclamation whether or not she concurs. Less often, the responsibility falls to a son. If it does and he is married, his wife falls heir to the responsibility. I have known only one unmarried son who, in spite of other siblings, took care of his aging mother with the devotion of a nurse and a saint. But that's rare.

More frequently, I suppose in the interest of family democracy, the poor parents are shuttled from sibling to sibling like migrant workers. God forbid! Your folks deserve *a home* even if it happens to be *in* someone else's. Of course, they should visit their scattered sons and daughters if they are well enough but, please, they should not be rotated.

I mentioned in Chapter 5, "Money Talks," that all siblings should contribute to the support of their parents if that is necessary. The burden should not fall only on the one who provides the shelter. Let me repeat that principle of fair play once again.

If the final decision is to have your parents move in with you, try to make the best of it. It may be rough going some days, but you should also have many wonderful experiences. Most problems should be minor and temporary. Your parents deserve the care that you and your immediate family can give, and you deserve the rewards that can come from being a caring child.

Hospital

Acute General Hospital

Today approximately one-third of those who are confined to acute general hospitals are over sixty-five years of age. This figure may vary up and down in your local hospital depending on the demography of your community and the services the hospital offers; however, it should be high enough to force you to think about what you would do if one of your parents required hospitalization. Who would take care of the one not hospitalized? Who would take care of the house if it was empty? Could you visit if the hospital was not in your community? What would happen if your parents were not able to resume the same lifestyle they enjoyed before? Who would handle your parents' financial affairs in the interim? These and other questions have to be raised and answered either now or later. Things will work out better if you are prepared. If such a crisis has not already occurred in your family, it will only be a matter of time.

We find there are abuses in the use of hospitals, particularly by the aged. Unfortunately, there are still older people who distrust hospitals and think of them only as places to die. While it is true that many deaths do occur in hospitals, many more cures take place, much suffering is relieved, and many patients with serious problems are granted years of happy and productive life. I concur that when the need is only for terminal care, hospitals can be cold, sterile, and regimented places to spend one's last days on earth. At times, however, symptoms can be so severe that the talents of the hospital counterbalance its impersonal touch. Actually, in most hospitals you will find a more gentle and caring environment than you perhaps anticipated. The talk around town will usually serve as a pretty good barometer of the care a hospital provides.

What concerns me most in hospital usage is when the high cost prevents a patient from receiving prompt treatment for an early breast cancer, a curable bowel tumor, or an operation to restore sight. I understand such financial problems, but cannot accept them. Money should not stand in the way of necessary medical treatment. Fortunately for the elderly, Medicare will soften the blow but not entirely remove it because of extra costs. If such fears interfere with your parents' care, search for a solution. Talk it over with the attending physician and with the hospital authorities. They have the ways and means of either solving most financial problems or knowing where help can be found.

While the greatest abuse of hospitalization is overuse, not underuse, blame for this can be placed on our culture, on our physicians, and on ourselves. We are a health- and hospital-oriented society, and in many ways that is good provided real medical necessity exists. It is wasteful, however, if the same care could be provided in less expensive facilities and even worse if the admission was not needed in the first place. Although such admissions are rare, they should be avoided. Often the pressure for admission comes from the patient or his or her family. I have known of individuals who wanted to park grandma in the hospital so the family could take a vacation. That might be a good idea, but don't expect the public taxpayer to pick up the tab through Medicare. Although the physician may find it more convenient and even more lucrative to treat patients in a hospital setting, that is not sufficient justification for an unnecessary admission. Remember, it is your family's money and your family's inconvenience. So don't pack your parents off to the hospital unless it is absolutely medically necessary.

Hospitals are accredited voluntarily by an organization called the Joint Commission on Accreditation of Hospitals. Its certificate of approval is one way by which you can determine if your parent is in an institution that meets national minimum standards. Why would you want anything less? So look for the certificate, which should be displayed in some public place within the hospital (probably in the lobby). Although separate from accreditation, hospitals often post some sort of a "Patients' Bill of Rights," which outlines the principles governing one's access to his or her own medical information, personal privacy, freedom of choice, and other matters protecting the rights of the patient. It also states the patient's responsibilities. If you are unfamiliar with hospital routines, this document should help you and your parent to understand what to expect.

Getting admitted to a hospital can be a disturbing experience to elderly people, particularly if they are uncomfortable or seriously ill at the time. They will worry about their future, their spouse, their belongings, and some of the most insignificant things you can imagine. Therefore, help your parent through this trying time and particularly through the necessary maze of being admitted into a hospital. You probably will be better able to handle things such as identifying information, insurance coverage, next of kin, and similar matters than your upset mother or father. Try to imagine what must be going through their minds. They certainly are not humming, "Happy days are here again." So stay with them. Help them. Give them time to adjust. Do not just dump them off at the admitting office and run.

Visit your parents during their confinement. Most do, but try to use your imagination to create some pleasant expectations other than another bumpy ride to X-ray. When I was still quite young, my mother was hospitalized for an elective operation. I arranged with a florist to deliver a single rose each day so that as her stay progressed, she would accumulate a nice bouquet. What an effect it had! Not only did my mother look forward to the next day, but the nurses got caught up in the happy web of anticipation. I doubt if a florist would accept such an order today, but try to think up some little gimmick to keep your parent's mind off of today and on tomorrow. It can be one piece of a homemade puzzle delivered each day, a series of cards, telephone calls, pictures drawn by the grandchildren—almost anything simple but loving.

Don't forget the day of discharge. In Chapter 16, "Things of the Spirit," I will consider how to deal with the death of your parent whether in the hospital or at home, but now let us be more optimistic. Let us assume that the hospital stay had a happy ending. In such cases do not just offer to drive the patient home. Once again help your mother or father through the necessary maze. Fortunately, this time everybody will be in a better mood. Count yourself lucky.

Increasingly hospitals are beginning to offer many services other than bed care alone. They present all sorts of classes on the prevention of disease and on coping with illness once it occurs. They offer physical, occupational and speech therapy. Much of the radiation and chemotherapy for cancer is now given on an outpatient basis, and most laboratory, X-ray, and other special examinations are available on a doctor's order without climbing into a bed. I predict that over the next decade we will see many, many changes in the delivery of health care, and they may well affect your parents long before they affect you.

Ambulatory or Day Surgery

Today many hospitals perform ambulatory surgery, also called *outpatient* or *day surgery,* for a long list of less complicated procedures. This means that the patient goes to the hospital early in the morning without breakfast, has his or her operation under general anesthesia if necessary, and goes home by mid-afternoon. Think of the advantages, particularly if your mother or father is worried about staying. This method should be less expensive but may not be. Therefore, check it out and know what you are getting into. I do not want to go into hospital economics; believe me, it is complicated. When I graduated from medical school the charge for a ward bed in a teaching hospital was $4.00 per day, but now look at it. Of course, the care in those days was nothing like one would get today, so it is hard to make a just comparison.

The best way to avoid these high costs is to prevent illness by reducing one's risk factors, to use the facilities only when medically necessary, and to seek alternative ways of getting equal care in less expensive facilities. Ambulatory surgery should be one way to get quality treatment and at the least possible cost.

Psychiatric Hospital

The term *hospital* often conjures up the image of a general hospital with ambulances with flashing red lights backing up to its emergency room. The word may also refer to those institutions providing mental or psychiatric care whether for a short or a long stay or even on an outpatient basis. Admissions here are not too different from those to a general hospital. Similarly, these beds can be underutilized or overutilized. The big difference between general and psychiatric hospitals is in the commitment laws which can force the admission of a mentally ill person or can prevent it unless certain predetermined conditions are met. These laws differ from state to state, but generally they are designed to protect the rights of the individual and yet balance them with the rights of the public. If your mother or father should suffer sufficient mental illness to require this type of care, whether custodial or short-term, place the problem in the hands of your parent's doctor just as you would if he or she needed the services of a general hospital. The physician might need to consult with the medical staff of the psychiatric hospital, but it is his or her responsibility to find a solution, not yours. Many such admissions follow an acute altercation involving the police, an episode the family cannot handle within their own resources, or a slowly progressive deterioration of the individual's ability to coexist with the rest of society. But you will know when it is time to seek help.

As I mentioned in Chapter 11, "The Drugs They Take," mental derangement may be induced by drugs or systemic disease. Under such circumstances, medical, not psychiatric, care is required. Again, your parent's doctor should be able to sort these out. But if a mental hospital is needed, do not look at it with fear or embarrassment. Mental illness is not a sin—it is a disease as real as the measles. Treat it as you would any other illness.

Rehabilitation Hospital

Scattered throughout the country, primarily in large cities or their surrounding suburbs, are special hospitals designed to provide rehabilitation services to those physically incapacitated by recent illness or injury. When the acute phase is over and the patient is sufficiently stabilized so that he or she can be cared for either at home or in some other facility offering a lower level of care, the patient is discharged. Since strokes and spinal cord injuries require this kind of treatment, one or both of your parents may sooner or later be admitted to such a special facility. Many larger hospitals offer much the same type of service, but the exclusive rehabilitation hospitals offer the advantages of specialization, lower costs, group motivation, and often more individual attention.

The purpose of rehabilitation regardless of site is to reduce the disability by maximizing whatever function remains and by constructively altering the way one looks at his or her limitations. These institutions offer a full range of services: medical, nursing, physical therapy, occupational therapy, speech therapy, recreational therapy, social service, as well as many of the other support services found in a general hospital.

Most physicians have seen examples of two patients with the same disability, one returning to reasonable activity, the other bedridden or, at least, home-bound. The difference was entirely in the quality of the rehabilitation each received. Since rehabilitation is a recognized medical specialty, most general physicians and surgeons are not trained in such techniques. Consequently, demand that your parent get the best care possible. Imagine how helpful it would be to you and how great the psychological gain would be to your father and mother if through proper training they could take care of their own toilet needs, could feed themselves, could dress without help and could get in and out of bed on their own. Give your parents that advantage. If it is not offered, ask for it.

Day Hospital

Although the day hospital concept started in England in 1952, it is rapidly taking hold in this country. It is a system of care for the elderly combining the best of rehabilitation with the social and economic advantages of living at home. It permits someone like your mother or father recovering from a recent disability or mobility problem to be transported to a central facility offering all the services of a rehabilitation hospital. The difference is that by mid-afternoon the patient returns home. The frequency of visits varies but may start at three to five times a week and drop to once a week as improvement occurs. When the maximum benefit is reached, usually within three months, the patient is discharged. Without such a facility, many elderly patients would be confined to hospitals or nursing homes or, if cared for at home, would be denied rehabilitation.

Although the pure day hospital is designed as a rehabilitation facility, I would not be surprised to see a limited "respite" function added whereby a patient with a chronic illness could spend the day with other essentially home-bound friends, giving both the patient a social outlet and the caregiver at home a needed respite from the chore of being constantly on duty.

Nursing Home

Nursing homes provide care for those who no longer need the expensive diagnostic or therapeutic services of an acute general hospital, but who, at least in most cases, require long-term care because they are either too difficult to handle at home, or no one at home is willing or able to give them the care they need.

Less than 5 percent of those over sixty-five years of age are in nursing homes at any one time, yet that is a sizable 1.3 million older people. Nevertheless, the odds are slim that your parents will ever be admitted to one. However, the odds increase as your parents get older, as one or the other becomes widowed or as financial and social problems increase.

You might be better forewarned if you could match your parents' present health problems with those which are most frequently seen in nursing homes. The top five most frequent medical problems in decreasing order are: arteriosclerosis, or hardening of the arteries, senility, heart trouble, severe arthritis, and strokes. Of course, many patients have multiple problems. Injuries, particularly hip fractures, account for a considerable number, but usually such stays are relatively short. There are some cancer patients, but many of these spend most of their terminal illness either at home, in a hospital, or, as I will discuss later, in a hospice.

The care which nursing homes provide is divided into two levels: *skilled* and *intermediate*. Lesser levels of care are termed *residential* or custodial, but for practical purposes they are not what most people associate with the term "nursing home." Homes that provide skilled nursing care are referred to in the medical jargon as *Skilled Nursing Facilities* (SNFs). Those offering a lower level of care are called *Intermediate Care Facilities* (ICFs). Although these levels of care are defined in lengthy federal and state regulations, in essence skilled care requires a registered nurse around the clock, seven days a week. Intermediate care requires nurse supervision during the ordinary workweek day shift, while care at other times is provided by aides or practical nurses. Most homes provide both levels, but in geographically separate nursing units. This is a distinct advantage, because a patient often flows back and forth between SNF and ICF as his or her condition changes.

If your parent is to be admitted to a nursing home, be careful how he or she is classified. The tendency of both relatives and physicians is to try to make the patient eligible for care in the skilled facilities because Medicare, with some limitations, picks up the tab. Many people are unaware that Medicare does not pay for ICF care on the assumption that technically it is not acute medical care. However, if the nursing home sees on arrival or shortly thereafter that the patient does not meet SNF criteria, they will redesignate him or her to ICF. They do this to assure that Medicare reimbursement will not be denied retroactively because of an inappropriate classification. Obviously this is to your advantage as well as to theirs. Otherwise, you might be confronted with a large bill you didn't anticipate. You would be surprised at how many families find it convenient to care for a patient at home when federal funds melt away.

Actually, few nursing home patients qualify for SNF care. This is often a crushing blow to those who have for years erroneously believed that, once on Medicare, their financial worries are over should they ever have to go to a nursing home. Medicaid, the program for the medically indigent, will pay for both levels of care if such care is medically necessary. However, the individual has to be essentially destitute to be eligible for such payments.

Patients in nursing homes are cared for by either their own physician or by a physician assigned to them by the home. I have no strong preferences. What I do recommend is a physician who has knowledge of and respect for the elderly. Unfortunately, there are too few such individuals, and although we constantly hear and read that there is more interest in this field by the young graduates of medical schools, I have seen little improvement so far. The reasons for this are complex but seem to revolve around three factors:

1. The low financial return
2. The emotional drain of constantly working with chronically ill people
3. The relatively little trickle-down effect that recent research on aging has had on clinical practice

I am still hopeful that in the future things will improve. In the meantime, try to obtain for your parents a physician who will be anxious to work aggressively on their behalf. It will make a significant difference. Incidentally, the charges this physician will make, whether selected by you or assigned by the home, will be in addition to those rendered by the facility. They may be covered by Part B of Medicare or by Medicaid for those eligible—but always check first so that there will be no misunderstanding.

Many homes are accredited by the Joint Commission on Accreditation of Hospitals using special nursing home standards. In addition, they are licensed by your state, so check with the appropriate division of your state government to help you identify the homes which do not have any violations against them. Word of mouth is also helpful in selecting a good nursing home, but it is not absolute. I have heard families swear by and others swear at the same home. Apparently, personalities and prejudices play a large role in judging competence.

Since religion probably plays a major role in your aging parents' life, you and they may wish to find a nursing home operated by people of their own faith. Although homes cannot discriminate in the admission of patients, there is still a recognizable aura that might either attract or repel certain applicants.

All nursing homes have arrangements with other community health care facilities for whatever backup services a patient might need, such as hospitalization, laboratory tests, or X-ray examinations. They may have their own physical therapy department or use outside community services. Consequently, do not feel that you are putting your mother or father out to pasture. Fear not, he or she will receive whatever care is needed.

Nursing homes in many parts of the country have felt the sting of a bad press. Without knowing the facts, people have built up prejudices against them. That is unfortunate because it may have already tarnished your opinion—but even worse, the opinions of your parents. Be assured that there are many fine physicians, nurses, social workers, aides, housekeepers, food service people, maintenance men, and other personnel who give their full devotion to the elderly patients under their care. Management is often enlightened, and the volunteers are as dedicated as they are elsewhere in the health care field. If you ever have to search for an acceptable home, you will find that in contrast to the large majority of hospitals operated as nonprofit institutions, some three-fourths of the nursing homes are profit-making. Do not make any categorical judgments about which is preferable. If the operators are trying to skim off too much profit or the religious leaders lack administrative skills, the care rendered could be unacceptable. Visit the home; talk to the administrator; look it over. Talk to some of the patients and their families. You will soon be able to make an informed judgment. However, although you should not expect a resort hotel, do not accept a warehouse for the handicapped and elderly. It should be a clean, busy, and caring place, even if the guests are not in prime shape. Be realistic, although I admit that the line between good care and bad is often difficult for many to determine. People often judge nursing home care by standards they might use when caring for young or healthy individuals. That is not quite fair. Many procedures—such as tying an elderly patient in a wheelchair—can shift from good to bad by when it is done, how it is done, and why it is done. If you do not understand something, ask. If the answer seems logical, accept it. If it seems cold, perfunctory, or unsatisfactory, challenge it.

As you may know, nursing homes are carefully regulated by state governments, and if Medicare payments are involved, there are additional federal requirements as well. This should give you and your parents considerable protection. Many states have also adopted a "Bill of Rights for Patients" which, like that for hospitals, protects the residents in an environment in which, if one is not careful, individuals could easily become dehumanized.

However, do not expect your parents to be happy about being admitted to a nursing home. They will resist, plead, cry, even revile your motives to the point that you may think it best to give in. You will feel guilty, selfish, even cruel. Yet if your decision was sound in the first place, it still is—so stick to it. If your decision was selfish, calloused, and unnecessary before, it still is—so reconsider it, but beware. Being sent to a nursing home even in the patient's best interest may be so devastating that the patient's condition can actually deteriorate, and on rare occasions may even lead to premature death. However, adequate preparation should minimize such adverse effects. Once the move takes place, reason usually prevails within the next few days. Friendships are made with staff and other residents, the advantages are recognized, and the inevitability is accepted. You will probably make your first visit with trepidation only to find a complete change from the time you tearfully said goodbye on the day of admission. It follows much the same scenario as a child's first day at school.

Unfortunately, in some individuals there may never be a full acceptance. An elderly bachelor who had been my scoutmaster when I was young entered a nursing home voluntarily. It seemed like good planning, but once there he didn't like it. He felt he lost his freedom, so he left. Some years later at about ninety years of age he wandered back because he just couldn't handle the requirements of living alone. He had been mugged twice on going to the store, one time suffering a broken hip. He had been robbed once when he fell asleep in a bus station, and he almost set his apartment on fire too many times to count. During my visits to his small quarters, I never did see his bed made or his clothes hung up, yet the acceptance of his need for proper care came to him very slowly. Even after he was finally admitted the second time, I cannot remember a visit in which he did not ask me to help him get out again and back into a small apartment. He always felt somebody was cheating him, yet he was in one of the finest homes in the area, one with a ten-year waiting list. Although the old gentleman could not remember to zip his fly, he never accepted the loss of independence the home imposed. Perhaps someone with an untrained eye or ear might have taken his remarks as a justifiable criticism of the nursing home and ridden forth to reform the place. Fortunately, I knew better.

Even if alone in this world, as was this old man, few nursing home patients are really abandoned. A long line of children, grandchildren, other relatives, friends, and even volunteers visit them and brighten their day. They come on their birthdays, they celebrate holidays, provide snacks, and, if possible, take them out for brief excursions. Although the elderly should not be institutionalized without solid justification, when it is necessary, accept it. Help your mother or father to accept it and make the best of it. Under those circumstances, there is really no alternative, and when it is done, do not feel guilty about it. You did what was right.

Please do not confuse this use of the word "alternative" with what is commonly called *alternative care*. This latter term refers to the many services that can be brought to a patient to help keep him or her at home, thus avoiding institutionalization. These services include visiting nurses, home health aides, homemaker aides, Meals-on-Wheels, physical therapists, social workers, and more. The use of these professionals in the home is not only less expensive, but the aging individual is not uprooted from his or her beloved home. I certainly recommend such services whenever they are available. Unfortunately, there still may come a time when the patient cannot be properly cared for in a home setting even with these services. At that time, admission to a hospital, nursing home, or hospice may be the only alternative.

Hospice

The hospice movement, as well as the day hospital, came to this country from England. The term was lifted from a French word for a shelter for travelers which, in turn, was derived from *hospitium*, the Latin word for hospitality. However, this new use of the word in its purest form refers not to a place but rather to an innovative method of caring for a limited number of selected terminally ill patients, 90 percent of whom are victims of cancer. While not focusing on a cure, hospice care provides an intensive level of medical, emotional, and spiritual support rendered by an interdisciplinary team of professionals and volunteers who aim to make the patient's last days both comfortable and meaningful, and who at the same time help the survivors with their anticipatory grief and bereavement. As the patient's medical or environmental condition improves or deteriorates, he or she may be shifted back and forth between a special inpatient facility, often loosely called a hospice because of the type of care the institution provides, and their own home where they receive "hospice care."

The advantage of this method of terminal care lies primarily in the skills and attitudes of the people rendering such care. They are specialists who know what to say and do. Because of their psychological training, they avoid the mistakes many of the rest of us tend to make at such trying times. They are more practiced in pain control. They, indeed, bring quality of life to the patient's last days and comfort to the family and friends who must share the loss. Some patients do not need this special medical and emotional support but rather are adequately or even better served by the more traditional methods of care. Others, unfortunately, are not eligible for hospice care because of the nature or severity of their illness. Your parent's own physician is the one to consult about the availability of hospice care or about its appropriateness for your mother or father.

Although Medicare rules are subject to change, at least for the moment the costs of certain hospice services provided in both an institutional setting and in the patient's home are reimbursable within certain time and dollar limits.

I cannot predict the future of the hospice movement, but I have my guess. It arose as most movements do because of an unmet need. Up until recently, hospitals have treated the dying with tremendous scientific zeal but with little warmth. In addition, the costs were astronomical. When possible, hospitals would gladly transfer such terminally ill patients to nursing homes, where for all practical purposes they were out of sight and out of mind. This created the need for something better. Fortunately, acute general hospitals are now catching on. They recognize that if comfortable and compassionate care can be given in a hospice, it can also be given in a hospital. Because most terminally ill patients do not need expensive diagnostic or therapeutic services, these acute care hospitals are beginning to create separate hospice nursing units within their own facilities and will soon develop the necessary components for caring for such patients in their own homes. Although many existing free-standing hospices may eventually disappear or be absorbed, their valuable function will certainly continue. Your parents may be their beneficiaries.

Summary

At a time in your aging parents' lives when they are least able to handle change and disruption, they may be subjected to the frightening experience of being moved out of their familiar surroundings. That certainly makes for strike number one. Illness and the prospect of death add two more strikes. Yet, don't count the elderly out. You will find that most of them will eventually adjust to their new environments with surprising grace. That fact alone is a powerful tribute to the resiliency of old age. Such behavior should help you not only to better understand the aging process but also to challenge you to shower upon your aging parents all the love and care that you can possibly muster. This is particularly true if they have to leave their own home, temporarily or permanently, for a home away from home.

CHAPTER 14

Playing It Safe

A recent survey of a group of elderly citizens revealed that their major concern was crime and safety. Yet as we faculty members discussed this report with some medical students, we concluded that there must have been some misunderstanding. We could not believe that health was not the greatest single concern of the elderly. However, with that one proviso, we accepted the fact that your aging parents are gravely worried about crime and their own safety. The elderly expect ill health. "It comes with the territory," as they would say. It's God's will, part of life. On the other hand, crime is not a part of normal life. It cannot be God's will. It is not a just reward for such deserving individuals. Many people of your parents' age grew up in a time when doors were unlocked and streets were safe. Regrettably, that way of life is gone in much of our nation.

There are a number of reasons why your parents are more vulnerable to both crime and accidents than you or the younger members of your immediate family. The elderly may have reduced vision or hearing; they may be physically frail and weak; they may be unsteady on their feet, even partially disabled; they may be forgetful, even gullible; or they may overestimate their abilities. Although most people recognize these limitations and like good Boy Scouts try to help the elderly, criminals use the same weaknesses for their own selfish advantage.

But before we discuss crime, let us concentrate on some of the threats to your parents' safety within their own home. In order of frequency, at least for the elderly, falls account for the largest number, next come burns and scalds, and as a poor third and fourth, poisonings and suffocation.

Falls account for approximately 80 percent of the deaths from these four top causes, and although statistics on nonfatal falls are less reliable, the figures are probably just as depressing. As might be expected, deaths from falls in individuals seventy-five years of age and above are almost four times as high as those between sixty-five and seventy-four. We tend to use the word "accidents" when referring to these unhappy events, as if they were unavoidable. Rather it would be more appropriate if we referred to them as "something unplanned." Actually, most are avoidable and preventable, and they occur because of carelessness. Most should never happen.

However, when they do, they can be very serious. As you know from the section on osteoporosis, your parents' bones may be much softer and weaker than they were in their younger years. This may be particularly true in your mother's case. A tumble which in the past might have caused her no real damage will at her present age cause not only fractures and internal injuries but expose her to all of the medical complications frequently following such trauma in an elderly individual.

Consequently, why not designate yourself, surreptitiously if necessary, as your parents' safety officer? As you visit their home, make a conscientious effort to hunt for potential hazards such as loose floor coverings; lamp cords that cross traffic lanes; small dark obstacles such as foot stools, sewing baskets, or piles of books or magazines; poorly lit stairs; absence of handrails; or anything else that might provoke an accident. The bathroom, particularly the bathtub, is one of the most dangerous spots in the whole house, so look for antiskid strips in the tub and grab bars on the wall. Do away with tiny rugs or mats on potentially slippery floors. Large, flat mats with nonskid backing or wall-to-wall carpeting will usually prevent slipping.

When you think of other bathroom dangers, your first concern should be the temperature of the hot water. Next check for portable heaters that are too close to curtains and towels; electrical appliances that are too near a water source; breakable glass containers of all sorts; and sharp scissors and razors which take on a special threat to those with poor eyesight. Also look for cleaning solutions and toiletries that might be confused with medicines. Keep them separate.

When people first feel faint from heart attacks, internal bleeding, strokes, and most other medical emergencies, they tend to retreat to the bathroom. Consequently, that is where rescue squads find many of their patients and where you should look if your parents do not answer the door.

As we catalog general household dangers, let us not forget unsteady stools or steps used to find items stored beyond one's normal reach. Careless use of such devices or the use of chairs or other inappropriate household articles not built for safe climbing are invitations to falls that can cause damage not only to limbs but to heads and internal organs.

If you spot any of these potential hazards, do not just correct them when nobody is looking, because if you do, the foot stool will be right back next to the doorway, the pretty little throw rug will again brighten that drab stretch of slippery floor, and the little radio will again be placed next to the bathtub where it will play its tunes while your folks sit and soak one note away from disaster. Try teaching some preventive medicine. Warn your parents of the dangers in their home, and show them that you are concerned with their health and safety. Suggest whatever alternatives appear possible and try to have them establish safe habits. Most falls, whether at home or outside, can be prevented if one is constantly on guard. A little informal chat on safety can be brought up at some opportune time when it does not appear that you are either butting in or are distrustful of their capacity to take care of themselves. A little warning surely beats a long hospital stay.

Although injuries by fire rank second in frequency to falls, the damage and suffering they cause cannot be matched. Fire not only destroys exposed tissues, but the heat and burning gases can so seriously sear and poison the lungs that a person may well succumb to respiratory failure long before any burns to the skin are suffered. As you read so often in newspapers, people in hotel fires usually die from fumes, not flames.

Scalds, caused by wet heat, are no less severe than burns and are generally more extensive by the very nature of cascading liquids. Water at 120° Fahrenheit can cause a third-degree burn in ten minutes, at 130° in ten seconds, and at 158° in one second. If water is steaming, you know that it must be above 212°, so there will be no time to avoid a dangerous scald. Consequently, help your parents set their water heater to 120°. It is the best way to prevent scalds and may even save them some money in utility bills.

Whereas the body has a wonderful healing power that in many instances restores an injured part to normalcy, this is not true with deep third-degree burns or scalds where the layers of the skin are actually cooked through. If recovery of function does occur, it is only after a long and painful period of hospitalization. Therefore, pay attention to fire hazards in your parents' home, and while you are at it, check your own home as well.

If your parents do not have as many smoke detectors or fire extinguishers as their home requires, buy some for their birthday or for some other gift-giving occasion. Such detectors are required in public homes for the elderly. Since your parents' house is a home for the elderly, why should they be denied any less protection? Smoke alarms save lives. Once your parents have these gadgets, help them place them in the proper locations. To be most effective, smoke alarms should be mounted at the top of stairs, in the bedroom hallway, and at any other spots where smoke or heat might accumulate. Obviously, they should not be placed near the stove or fireplace, or they will be going off constantly.

Fire extinguishers should be the type that can control paper, electrical, and oil fires, as well as being easy for the elderly to handle. These extinguishers should be placed near the stove, furnace, fireplace, and similar hazardous locations, but not so close that they cannot be reached in time of need. However, time should not be lost trying to put out a fire that is patently beyond one's ability to control. Warn your parents to get out and then call for help.

Of equal importance to the availability of these safety devices and to the instruction in their use and maintenance is a fire evacuation plan. If your parents did have a fire, chances are they would not have enough time to think about avenues of escape. They will have to react instinctively. Therefore, as you develop your own evacuation plan, help your parents outline one for themselves. And remember, if they sleep in separate rooms as many elderly do, that must be given special consideration. If your parents have not developed a plan by now, they probably won't in the immediate future—so remind them.

Your safety survey should identify such fire hazards in your parents' home as the stove, oven, fireplace, portable or space heaters, central heating system, garage, lamps, candles, the storage of flammable solutions, and many others. Defective equipment should be repaired or replaced, and safety precautions should be taken for every other hazard. The dropping of live ashes or butts into overstuffed chairs and sofas causes many fires, some fatal, as does smoking in bed.

You are probably familiar with these warnings, and chances are your parents are as well. Reminders are everywhere. So why are there so many fatal fires? It is because most people don't do anything about fire protection until it is too late. Well, now is the time. Do it! A fire is a tragedy you should try to avoid at all costs.

If you recall, the third most frequent cause of accidental death in the elderly is poisoning. Poor vision and mental confusion can easily account for this. The secret here is to store poisons away from foods and medicines. However, even if you do, poisoning can still occur if drugs or home remedies are used in the wrong dosage or inappropriate manner.

Suffocation or asphyxiation, the fourth cause, is usually due to carbon monoxide leaking from a faulty furnace or unvented space heaters, or toxic gases created by an actual fire. The family car running in a closed garage can also be an instrument of death, either accidental or intentional. Carbon monoxide can kill with no warning to the victims, no odor, no coughing, no acute distress. Small doses over a prolonged period might cause headaches, but usually symptoms are lacking. It is a silent killer.

Other types of home accidents vary and often depend upon the individual's lifestyle. A farm environment, hobbies involving mechanized tools, the use of electric fans and other appliances, as well as extreme climatic conditions all add to the possibility of accidents. No, the home is not a very safe place unless care and thought are constantly used. Make sure the home of your aging parents is as safe as is reasonably possible. Perhaps you cannot stop a meteorite from hitting one of your parents, but you can stop just about everything else.

Yet safety is not only the prevention of accidents. It includes the availability of help in times of crisis. One of the constant worries of your parents, and I suppose of all of us, is the thought of facing some emergency and not being able to summon help. Heart attacks and strokes come to mind even more vividly than do accidents. In most retirement homes, someone on every hallway is designated as a monitor to make sure that he or she sees every resident every day unless they are otherwise accounted for. Furthermore, many of these institutions have emergency alarm systems in every room or apartment by which help can be summoned. Some communities have organizations that provide much the same security but by telephone. Under that system, the elderly individuals must call their monitoring office before a certain time each morning or they will be called. If no answer is obtained, the police will be notified. I referred earlier to loneliness. The fear of being stricken with no one knowing about it is merely an extension of that basic insecurity. Are your parents that vulnerable? If so, help them seek out a monitoring service, secure one of the many types of panic alarm systems, or persuade a neighbor to look out for them.

Many community rescue squads support a program called "Vial of Life." In part it started because of a recognized need but also because these squads found themselves inundated with empty plastic vials that once held sterile syringes six or seven inches long. Since these empties seemed too good to throw away, somebody got the idea that the elderly, particularly those living alone, should fill out a form giving all their pertinent identifying information along with such medical facts as diagnoses, medications, allergies, name of their physician and next of kin, and then slip it into one of these vials with a bright red sticker attached. The whole thing is then placed in the refrigerator, a place common to every household. If the rescue squad were ever called to the home, they would immediately know where to look for the "Vial of Life" and would not have to waste time searching for vital information. If your community does not have such a service, your rescue squad or local hospital, both of which have the empty vials, should be stimulated to start such a project. It could save your parents' lives.

Repeated accidents, illnesses, or even close misses involving your parents might suggest that your father or mother can no longer live independently and must either have some live-in companion or move into some other environment capable of providing a higher degree of safety. That is a tough decision, but at times it must be made. Often a minor accident or a small fire will make the necessary point, but as I have said before, the will to live independently is strong and at times irrational. It may take a lot of talking, but do not rush the decision or dominate the discussion. Work up to it so that there will be at least some intellectual acceptance of the plan, if not outright pleasure. Your father and mother will not find it easy to swap their independence for some unknown facility, even if it does offer increased security.

Falls, burns and other accidents can occur outside the home as well as within. The same carelessness prevails and the same cautions are appropriate. Falls occur on broken pavement and slippery surfaces; burns result from fires in trash piles or the careless barbecuing of hamburgers; and injuries follow the thoughtless handling of lawn mowers and other power equipment. Do not forget the careless pedestrian. Except for little children, most pedestrian accidents involve the elderly. In cold climates you have to think of hypothermia (low body temperature) and frostbite. In more tropical climes, beware of sunburn and heat stroke. I can only repeat, "Caution, caution, caution."

Turning now to another subject, I am sure that you are well aware that all so-called "street crime" does not necessarily occur on the street. Much of it invades the premises of the aged themselves. Although you often hear the elderly express fears about going out of the house, a greater fear exists that a criminal might actually enter the sanctity of their own home. The vulnerability of your parents, their frailty, poor vision, poor hearing, and gullibility make them easy marks for the criminal determined to get inside their home. Entrance need not be by force. Many criminals innocently approach the front or back doors in the guise of salespeople, motorists in distress, meter readers, building inspectors, and all sorts of uninvited guests. In many neighborhoods, these visitors are what they say they are, but too often they are not. Once they find that the elderly person is alone, they push their way in, overpower the occupant, cut the phone wires, and take what they want. If there is resistance, they do not hesitate to use force. Not all intruders are after your parents' TV or stereo. Some are sick, intent on rape. Age does not seem to be a factor. Any defenseless female will serve their perverted purpose. The trick here is not to let such criminals in. Your parents should always recognize who is at the door before opening it. If the door is solid, a one-way peephole should be installed. If an intercom system is not available, suggest that the stranger shout his or her message through the closed door. This may be awkward, but it's safe.

Of course, not all criminals walk through open doors. Many break in with or without the occupant present, but once in, they are no better mannered than those who entered by deceit. As your parents' safety officer, you might check the security of the whole house, including the doors, windows, basement, lighting, vision of strangers, and so on.

In recent years the advice on home security has received much publicity. If your parents belong to a senior citizens' club of some kind, they will probably be offered many governmental and private pamphlets on how to make their home more secure. In addition, most metropolitan police departments offer safety programs to community groups and even provide individual home inspections. Many of their suggestions can be accomplished at little or no cost, and others with some modest expenditure, but the extra measure of safety makes it worthwhile. Some police departments have Crime Prevention and Victim Assistance Programs which first try to prevent crimes against the elderly, but if they occur, try to help the victims as much as possible. Find out if one of these services is in your parents' neighborhood, because it may provide the answer you and your parents are looking for.

Depending on where your parents live, their neighborhood may be a haven of tranquillity or a seething jungle. It is distressing to see so many elderly held prisoners in their own homes by fear of street crime. The most common is the violent kind, the muggings and purse snatchings. Unfortunately, some of these so-called "minor crimes" cause major disabilities or even death when inflicted on the elderly, whose bones are brittle, hearts are weak, and organs are devoid of the padding of youth.

There is little protection from such attacks. Losses can be minimized by not carrying large sums of money or valuables, but the best defense, of course, is a strong companion. That job may fall to you, to one of your strong teenage children, or to some obliging neighbor. Your parents can only partially reduce their exposure to street crime by using their car, provided their home can be safely entered behind garage doors that are opened and closed by a remote-controlled device. The few steps from the car to the front or back door without protection may be somewhat less hazardous than walking all the way because the criminal would need to use precise timing, but if a pattern of coming and going is firmly established, an enterprising crook can decipher it. Your parents are particularly vulnerable if they are seen leaving a store or the teller's window of a bank with a fistful of money. This is sufficient bait for some thief to follow them home and plan a grisly blitzkrieg. If your parents have possessions they want to keep, do not let them flaunt them in front of strangers.

As I said before, the best protection against crime when either walking or driving is to be accompanied by a strong companion. Some communities have a paid or volunteer Neighborhood Security Aide Program which provides the elderly with escort services to and from stores, churches, and other public places. Others have Neighborhood Watch Programs where each resident serves as the eyes and ears of his or her own immediate area and reports to the police any suspicious activity. Signs notifying that the area is under a Neighborhood Watch Program further add to the security. Some larger communities organize themselves more formally and assign residents on a rotating basis to patrol the area, some even being in direct contact with the police by portable two-way radios. The younger people in the neighborhood usually do not have the time to organize such programs. If it needs doing, urge your parents or some other elderly people in the neighborhood to take on the task. It will be good for them in a number of ways.

You may have heard of the program called "Project Whistle Stop," whereby community residents are given or told to buy whistles that they carry with them to summon help or to alert others of danger. "Screechers" serve the same purpose. Some recommend chemical mace, but it is outlawed in many jurisdictions. Actually, these devices in the hands of the elderly do not appear to be very effective weapons in the prevention of crime.

Therefore, if some kind of community protection is not available, a group of three or more elderly walking together might be the next best practice. It offers additional eyes and ears to warn of a possible attack, to give witness to the crime, and to describe the perpetrator. A large dog is helpful, but only if it is not the cat-chasing kind, because an unruly dog can do its own kind of mayhem. I will not soon forget two compressed vertebrae suffered when my own dog, a frisky little schnauzer, pulled me down on an icy driveway.

Some people try to avoid the possibility of their parents suffering street crime by doing their shopping for them. That's a nice gesture, but it inflicts its own kind of harm by robbing their parents of some of the independence they so desperately need. Most aging parents require the exercise, stimulus, and exuberance of shopping or visiting. You may drive them to their destination, but let them push their own grocery cart even at their intolerably slow pace. That's independence. Pawing through a cluttered purse to pay the cashier is independence. To bank in person instead of by mail is independence. To assist your parents with these chores will consume a lot more time, energy, and nail biting than if you did it yourself, but at what cost? Sure, during bad weather, illness, or when the needed item is one your parents do not care to shop for, go do your good deed. But don't overdo it.

Not all street crime is of the physical kind. Each year, always when the weather seems good and people are at their best, the newspapers carry a story about some poor old widow who was taken for her life savings by a con artist who convinced her that he or she had just found some money or was a bank investigator needing help. Stories such as these trap the unwary to hand over their money ostensibly for only a brief time but with the gamble of a big reward. How can you tell your parents not to be so gullible? Some middle-aged sons and daughters must not have taken the pains to broadcast the proper warnings. Well, now is the time to do your own broadcasting.

It may seem to you that I have constantly repeated that you should teach your folks this and warn them about that, and then begged you to do one thing after another. But I am not the only one. No less than the general manager for criminal investigation of the U.S. Postal Service recently issued the following warning to the nation's elderly: "Beware of frauds and schemes perpetrated through the mails." He indicated that the most common swindles aimed at the elderly were work-at-home deals, insurance frauds, debt consolidation loans, security schemes, worthless medical cures, fraudulent land sales, and nursing home frauds. However, I have also stressed that aging parents vary tremendously. Many do not need such warnings; many may not need such warnings when they are young-olds but may need them when they are old-olds; and many need them in one facet of their lives but not in others. But be mindful that every physician who has worked in a hospital emergency room has seen a parade of elderly people who were injured by accidents or victimized by crime. It is reasonable to think that the elderly themselves should have been savvy enough to avoid such predicaments, but apparently they were not. Therefore, we either have to let the carnage continue or try to stop it. My choice is to try to stop it by whatever means possible. I know of no magic solution, yet I do know that people learn best when there is both demonstration and repetition and when the need is real and timely, not abstract. Therefore, I urge you to be a good teacher and demonstrator if your parents appear vulnerable.

But, please, do not go overboard. Danger can never be eliminated. Freedom and risk have to be balanced. No parent would ever give up freedom or quality of life for safety or quantity of life. For example, an elderly gentleman I know cut his finger while slicing an apple. While it's true that his eyesight was not perfect nor was he steady of hand, should his family guarantee his safety by taking away his access to knives? Heavens, no! That is done to suicidal patients in mental hospitals but not to those who are just growing old. That old man learned his lesson. He now knows that he has to be more careful, but he still retains his freedom. However, if crime and safety are indeed priority concerns of your aging parents, their prevention should be your top priority as well. But not at the expense of reasonable freedom.

I would prefer not to write this short postscript to this chapter on how to protect your aging parents from harm, but facts demand it. As in any large section of society, there are a few bad apples. That is even true with the aged, but most were probably that way long before they grew old. Unfortunately, crime by, not to, the elderly can increase whenever responsible relatives or the community fail to monitor the needs of the elderly. There is some difference of opinion at the present time as to whether shoplifting has or has not increased among the elderly. Some say it has because they need food, clothing, and medications. These proponents claim that the elderly erroneously believe that the least embarrassing way of securing certain necessities of life is through quiet shoplifting. Others say there is no such evidence and, if they do shoplift, it is for silly things like costume jewelry. I do not know where the truth lies, so all I can do is to warn you to be on the alert. Do not wait until a desk sergeant in the police department calls you to tell you that your aging father or mother has a problem.

Your parents' lives and their possessions are valuable, too valuable to be lost needlessly. Therefore, protect both by playing it safe.

CHAPTER 15

The Gift
of Grandchildren

Photo by Virginia Kraucunas

Almost without exception, senior citizens love animals—the well-behaved, domesticated kind such as dogs and cats, but even more they love grandchildren. If they do not have their own, they will muscle in on somebody else's. Although learning to care for your aging parents concerns primarily you and your spouse, in this one unique situation your children will become intimately involved. Obviously, the relationship between grandparents and grandchildren varies with the ages of the children and to some extent with the ages of the grandparents, and it also varies with distance, with your parents' state of health, with differing lifestyles, and with as many other factors as a child's active mind can create. But in spite of these variables, the relationship is always a fascinating two-way road.

To those of you who may not have made a gift of grandchildren to your aging parents, this chapter may appear to have little relevance. However, the information it contains should not only help make you a more sympathetic middle-aged son or daughter, but it should also help you understand how your parents might react to any such deprivation. Furthermore, it may suggest some ideas on how you might ease the tension between you and them should any exist. In Chapter 2, I pointed out that conflicts over silly little things often crop up between adult children and their aging parents. Unfortunately, the lack of grandchildren can be one of those silly little things. Your parents may not understand or wish to understand why this is so. In fact, they may be incapable of understanding the reason and by constant harping on the subject create unnecessary friction. Therefore, try to keep communication open. Try to build some base of understanding. If you are past the childbearing years, there is little you can do about it biologically, but you might be able to work out a few vicarious substitutes. So, go ahead, finish reading the chapter.

Because the ages of grandchildren make such a difference in how they relate to their grandparents, it would seem best if we divided these special animals into five age groups:

1. From fetus to two years
2. Preschool
3. First grade through puberty
4. Puberty to legal majority
5. Old enough to produce great-grandchildren

Few grandparents will have the pleasure of witnessing all five stages, but they will relish to the fullest as many as the Lord will permit.

Although it needs little emphasis, the matter of distance colors this whole relationship. Proximity, the kind that exists in an extended family, provides the greatest and perhaps the most desirable interaction between the two. As each mile is interposed thereafter, the bond thins out. The grandparents' desire to see their grandchildren parallels the distance: the greater the distance, the greater the longing. Although mail, telephone, and pictures are weak substitutes for being together, they are links that can keep family relationships active and alive between visits. But nothing can take the place of face-to-face contact. One of the happiest days of my mother-in-law's last few months of life was when her grandson and his wife traveled over a thousand miles each way to permit her for the first and only time to cuddle her great-granddaughter in her arms and to feel the grasp of the baby's tiny fingers around her own. What an effort for such a few moments of ecstasy, but that moment of joy succinctly describes the feelings of all grandparents. Don't deny them those close encounters.

If distances are not prohibitive and visitation can be fairly regular, how might your children interact with your parents in each of the five time frames I previously mentioned?

From Fetus to Two Years

Unless you are also a grandparent, you may not fully realize how your own parents are going to react to the news that they are about to become grandparents. I can assure you that the news will be met with wild enthusiasm even if the due date is a little shy of the nine months since they paid for the wedding. The enthusiasm will diminish only slightly if they already have so many grandchildren that they can't keep the names straight. The knitting needles will begin to click, the telephone lines to friends and relatives you never knew will begin to hum, and someone along the line will give your mother a grandmother's photo album so that she can be prepared for the first pictures. Do not underestimate the emotion that news of a forthcoming grandchild can bring. You will be inundated with gifts, offers, advice, questions, and sly references to names.

Once the baby is delivered, the emotion heightens. Your parents will accept their privileged status during the hospital visiting hours and will bore the nursing staff with their gratuitous chatter. But let them wallow in the joy.

Once everybody is home, there will be no limit to their solicitation. They will visit at every opportunity, even baby-sit if given the chance. However, you must recognize that in spite of all their outpouring of love and devotion, your parents will want to enjoy the special status of being able to cuddle, feed, and even change diapers without any parental responsibility. They will want to be able to walk away when they become tired. Except in those tragic situations where grandparents are thrust in a position of bringing up a grandchild as substitute parents, they prefer to take their grandchildren in small and controlled doses. A screaming, wiggling infant can tire your aging parents and upset their comfortable routines. If you are visiting them in their home and your bundle of joy is at the climbing and grabbing stage, they will "child-proof" the place by removing everything breakable within the child's grasp. However, they will not feel comfortable until everything is back in its proper place. Their love should never be equated with their apparent need to absent themselves from the day-to-day responsibility for your children or for their need to live their own independent lives.

It is at this early stage of your child's development that lasting relationships will be established for better or for worse. Conflicts between you and your aging parents can come up during any of the five stages I have outlined, but all too frequently they start at this early age, particularly if the grandparents butt in too aggressively. I am amazed at how many times my students, after interviewing families with young children, report that there is a conflict between the grandmother and the mother over the rearing of the children. It is difficult for anyone to give advice unless the person knows the exact circumstances surrounding each problem, but the child is yours, not the grandparents', and you must do whatever you think is correct. Certainly, their suggestions should be considered—they may even be right. After all, experience does count. So if you can accept some of their ideas, fine—you will then be in a better position to reject those which you cannot. If a difference of opinion still exists, do it your way, but think of some method by which you can decompress the potential hard feelings. Unless the grandparents live in your home, their visits will be relatively brief, and many things can be postponed until they leave. If they do live either with you or close enough for daily contacts, then diplomacy is your only recourse. An explanation of the way in which you want to raise your children may get your point across. Refer to your doctor's advice, to the current literature, or to other factual material, but in no way criticize or belittle your parents' suggestions. Try to maintain a day-in-and-day-out consistency in your actions. If you do things one way when you are alone and another when your parents are around, the child will become so confused that there will be no peace for either of you.

It is easy to take grandparents for granted, to expect them to be available for baby-sitting, transportation, and all sorts of favors and chores. But watch it. Sparks can fly if they feel put upon or are made to look as if they are subject to your every beck and call. Yet I repeat, their tolerance for service on behalf of grandchildren is overwhelming.

You will be fortunate and probably rather typical if grandma acts like the loving soul she wants to be, enjoying the baby, squeezing, bragging, spoiling, and helping, provided it can be on her own terms. Grandpa will be no different except in the outward manifestations of building things, providing transportation, and taking pictures. There are many advantages to the infant and to you as parents at this stage in having grandparents around. Play it to the hilt. There never will be a more ecstatic time for all concerned.

Preschool

It is at this age that the child begins to recognize the family unit. They sense that grandparents are different from the neighbors. They recognize that they enjoy a special position within the household; treat family members with special affection; are permitted a certain element of control the neighbors do not share; are present on birthdays and holidays; bring gifts, send cards, and make cookies; take them to fun places, not to the doctor or barber; and praise them, read to them, and give them individual identity. Their grandparents' pictures are everywhere—if not on tabletops, at least in albums. Some thoughtful parents give their children a small box containing snapshots of their grandparents, other family members, family events, and of course of the children themselves. They are permitted to play with them much as they would with their toys or books. This helps to unite a family. The toddler takes this all in and responds with trust and affection.

These are good days for your parents. They can feel the love that the youngster now returns. They can start to impart to the child a code of conduct, a sense of history, and the child's first feeble recognition that people grow old. As the child learns to establish his or her own identity by saying "no," he or she will also confront your parents, hoping that they will reverse all unpopular decisions. In effect, the child will assume that your parents have veto power. You can only hope that they will vote your way, or sparks will fly.

The youngster's world begins to expand with your parents' help. He or she may be able to stay away from home overnight without any sense of insecurity. However, toddlers are busy little bodies and can easily tire out your parents. Watch out for that! Protect your parents when it appears that they may be tiring. Children, of course, do not recognize the lack of physical stamina their grandparents may have, and their desire to play horsie or roughhouse can make an older person as vulnerable to overexertion as any other type of heavy physical activity.

As much as a frisky puppy or a cuddly kitten can bring joy to the hearts of the elderly, there is no joy more dear than young grandchildren. At this age, they can respond, return affection, and relate in an active and meaningful manner with their grandparents. The fact that they are in essence their own flesh and blood makes for a unique and wonderful bond between preschoolers and grandparents.

First Grade Through Puberty

This is a period when the child's horizons expand still further. Grandparents become just one more set of stars in his or her expanding universe. Therefore, they get less attention but still hold a privileged place in the widening constellation.

Your parents may not only continue to be prime baby-sitters, but might actually stay with your children for prolonged periods while you and your spouse are on vacation, on a business trip or when your parents' home or vacation cabin makes a good respite from a hot summer. Meanwhile, they will participate and even offer incentives in your children's education and career planning. These may or may not parallel your own desires, so be alert.

Lifestyles may begin to clash at this age. Your youngsters' styles—of dress, eating habits, speech, music, manners, and many others—may not jibe with those of their grandparents. I once heard the results of a survey of what children at this age thought about older people, including, but not necessarily restricted to, their grandparents. In general, they thought that older people were grouches, mean, sickly, and "icky," whatever that means. Perhaps some are, but it might be wise to evaluate the impression your children have toward your parents and to the elderly in general. It would be better for all concerned if these impressions could be healthy, loving, and respect-ful. Give your child the proper guidance, and if your parents are begin-ning to seem grouchy and "icky" to you, see if some tactful advice might sweeten things up a bit. Emphasize the contributions your par-ents' generation have made to society and those which your own par-ents have made to your family. Stress the positive. At this stage, alienation of your children from their grandparents would be tragic for both. The development of sound and productive relationships within the family circle can help in the proper emotional growth of your chil-dren and it can clearly demonstrate your own care and love for your aging parents, a role model they could well emulate in the future.

Although there may be some negative aspects to the relationship between your children and your aging parents at this stage, there are also many blessings. It is the grandparents who most forcefully teach the children their sense of heritage. Anecdotal lessons in history, in the family's roots and traditions from far-off lands, the way you be-haved when you were a child, and even social civility can be imparted in a way no other teacher could accomplish. If ethnic foods are served, encourage your parents to explain their origin and how the recipes have been handed down through the generations. Have them do the same for dress, religious customs, and language. In addition to their ability to make history and geography come alive, grandparents are fountains of confidential information that children will ask no one else. Values are taught; character is built. Children without close con-tact with grandparents are children denied.

It will be during these years that your parents may first experi-ence serious illness and even death itself. If it occurs in the earlier years, the impact on your children will be minimal. Its meaning will be lost, because the comprehension is just not there. But during these school to puberty years, the experience will not be ignored by the in-quiring and maturing minds of your children.

In Chapter 10 I discussed how to care for the health of your par-ents. In Chapter 16, "Things of the Spirit," I will discuss problems surrounding their deaths. This chapter concerns only how you expose your children to these tragedies.

Tremendous feelings of ambivalence will well up within you. You will ask yourself, "How much should I tell the children? Are they emotionally ready to handle Grandma's or Grandpa's death? If I don't tell them, will they find out someplace else? What should I say if they ask where people go when they die? Should they see their grandpar-ents sick, suffering, shadows of their former selves? Should they go to the funeral? Should they go to the cemetery for the interment? Should their visit to the cemetery be left for sometime later? What if they ask what will happen to them when they get old? What if they ask if I am going to die and, if so, who will take care of them? Should I tell them the truth, the whole truth, or part of the truth? What if I tell them one thing and someone else tells them something different? Whom will they believe?"

Yes, these and dozens of other questions will crop up. As much as you might wish that such questions were unnecessary and that your parents could stay in perfect health so that there would be no need for such difficult conversations, you will not be that fortunate. Questions will be asked.

Your children will not be your only stumbling block. Your parents will have their own ideas about how the children should be informed about such matters. Their views, perhaps rooted in a different time and culture, may conflict with yours, forcing you onto an even more difficult tightrope. They might ask, "Let me see my dear grandchildren once more before I go. I want to kiss them goodbye, my precious darlings. God only knows how I hate to miss seeing them grow up." Or conversely, they might retreat in panic and want to die alone. "I don't want the children to see me this way. I want them to remember me when I could read to them, play with them, love them. God knows, not this way. Look at me, skin and bones. And the smell!"

I have no one simple answer. No two cases are quite the same. How you handle the problem will vary with the age and emotional maturity of the child in this rather broad span of years from the beginning of school to puberty. The younger the child, the more he or she will be satisfied with broad, general answers. The older the child, the more searching the questions and the more realistic the answers will have to be.

The geographical closeness of your children to their grandparents will be a dominant factor in the questions asked and the answers given. If there is no real closeness, the only question might be, "Won't I get a birthday present from Grandma or Grandpa any more?" If you are an extended family, the questions will be more searching. My suggestion here is not unlike answering questions about sex. Answer the child truthfully, but at age five or six you do not have to go through the mechanics of conception. The same reasoning applies here. A simple, truthful answer geared to the level of the child's understanding is sufficient. When the child has his or her questions answered satisfactorily, the questions will stop. If older, he or she will ask additional questions. In that case, move along the child's understanding further until he or she is again satiated.

A child's understanding might have been previously expanded by the illness or death of a pet, a close friend, or even a sibling. In these cases, the child will be partially prepared by the time your aging parents suffer their terminal accident or illness. Here again, the questions will be more searching as your child tries to find answers for questions that may have been churning in the back of his or her mind ever since the earlier experience. Again, a child must be answered with sufficient clarity to satisfy his or her legitimate curiosity.

The basic truth of life is that we are all mortal. There is no biological immortality of one single organism, regardless of how simple or how complex it might be. That fact must be learned, and, indeed, it usually is with the first squashed bug or dead bird found in the garden. But for most children, these are abstract truths. The death of their grandparents will be considerably more concrete. They will suffer the loss personally. They will empathize with the person because it will not be just some fearsome giant that Jack-in-the-Beanstalk slew. It will be their own grandma or grandpa. This in itself will stimulate another whole barrage of questions that must be answered.

How you handle these unpleasant realities will be rather subjective. Part of your answer will be based on experience, either firsthand or from someone you trust; part will be by instinct; and part will be forced on you by society. You will probably want to combine all of these to reach the proper answer. The one thing you cannot do is wish the problem away. You will have to make up your mind on how to proceed. However, do not hesitate to seek help. You may want to follow the instructions your dying parent or surviving spouse may have given you. Consult your pastor, priest, rabbi, or other religious leader. A funeral director may be able to tell you what others have done successfully and what may have created problems. It will be a big enough burden to share.

Personally, I believe in letting the children experience the normalcy of illness and death provided it is done in an atmosphere of love and maturity, not rage, guilt, or blame.

When I was eleven years old, my mother died. I can recall every detail of her illness and funeral, at least that to which I was privy. Although it saddened me, it did not scar me. It left me with many memories, vivid to this day, and while not pleasant ones, at least they are healthy and loving. I would have felt left out, denied, hurt if I had not been able to share in those last moments. But as I look back, there were many things about illness and death that I did not learn until years later, but then I was more fully prepared to accept and understand them. That is the way it should be.

The death of one or both of your parents at this stage of your children's development will be rough, but do not lie to your children. Do not try to soften the blow by saying, "God took Grandma because He needed her." That will only create a feeling of abandonment and insecurity. The child will wonder, "When will He need me, or Mom or Dad?" or "Why did He need her?" Don't cover up or pass the buck. Admit that serious illness can strike anyone and cut his or her life short. Do not portray death as either a punishment or a reward. Do not deny your children the opportunity to learn and to face the reality of life in a loving and understanding manner. And remember to shade your responses to the child's own level of maturity—to do otherwise may cause scars and deny the child his or her normal emotional growth.

The years of growth and maturity between the start of school and puberty may also be very happy and pleasant ones for the whole family. Illness and death may not come until much later. Regardless of whether these years are joyful or sad, they will impact upon your aging parents and upon your growing children. Try to make this special period a learning and loving experience.

Puberty to Legal Majority

By puberty, the character of the child has been cast. It is too late for the grandparents to continue to make any significant impact. The children may continue to use them as role models, but in many cases they have picked more relevant individuals. The generation gap will be exaggerated. Except for courteous encounters and the receipt of a few presents bilaterally, there will be reduced contact.

During these years, we begin to see a reversal of the roles between your parents and your children. Whereas your parents were on the giving end, except for the expressions of love the children obviously returned, they are now on the receiving end. Bit by bit the children will become the givers. If geographically close, they will be asked to help their grandparents, to take care of their yard, to run their errands, or to help them in dozens of different ways in and around the house. These are not the same endearing experiences as a warm lap or a romp in the yard. All of the fun is now gone. Lifestyles will begin to conflict, neither understanding the other. Emancipation will come swiftly with the license to drive a car, the right to vote, and the ritual of becoming a fully franchised individual.

Occasionally some very close and trusting relationships develop, particularly if your idealistic teenagers see that their grandparents or those like them are in any way being denied or hassled by society. Like knights in shining armor astride white steeds, they will joust for justice and fair play. They will picket, campaign, and go to bat for good causes. They will befriend and protect the underdog. The girls will work as candy stripers in hospitals and nursing homes, while their brothers will serve as escorts for the aged. Actually, these kinds of relationships, like all good relationships, benefit both sides. Certainly your parents will have a vigorous advocate and a reliable resource. In turn, the young people will develop a deep understanding of the elderly, their ups and downs, their assets, and their liabilities, but above all they will learn love and respect at a more mature level than ever before. It should help you when you become an aging parent.

Old Enough to Produce Great-grandchildren

By this time, most formal education is complete, the key interpersonal relationships are established, and the biological and psychological facts of life and death are well understood. The days when your parents served as teachers and baby-sitters are over. Your aging parents and your full-grown children will relate pretty much as mature adults. It is conceivable if one of your children is sickly or suffers from some permanent disability that your parents may once again become part of that child's support system rather than the other way around. Should that happen, the relationship will be less emotional and more altruistic.

If things go well, your parents will look forward to the next generation. The thought of great-grandchildren will tease their fantasies. If they come true, the loving and cuddling cycle will repeat itself. These are again good times for your parents.

If perchance something happens to you and your spouse before one or both of your parents pass on, your grown children may have to assume, along with the other remaining next of kin, the care of their grandparents as well as all of the legal responsibilities that may be required to handle their estates. I hope that you have prepared them for the unexpected.

Although your parents may have traveled through these five stages of their own grandchildren's growth with grace, good health, and joy, they may still seek out children other than your own. We discussed in Chapter 8 how many of the elderly do volunteer work in day care centers, in hospital pediatric wards, churches, summer camps, and agencies of all kinds. Interestingly, there is a new development in Minnesota which brings young children and the elderly in even closer relationship. They have built a day care center right smack in the middle of a retirement village, across the hall from the residents. It approximates for both the children and the seniors many of the well-known benefits of the extended family.

Although there is no biological immortality, children and particularly grandchildren can assure here on earth a type of immortality that is satisfying and comforting to your aging parents. You have bestowed this gift. Don't let it tarnish or wear thin.

CHAPTER 16

Things of
the Spirit

*T*he title of this chapter will mean different things to different people. I expect that. Spiritual things work that way. Consequently, you may include in your list of spiritual things whatever stirs the spirit within your own soul. Meanwhile, grant me the privilege of telling you what I had in mind.

Organized religion tops my list. In one form or another, religion sustains most of the elderly. Yet if you were to deal closely with people of all ages and of all backgrounds as most physicians do, you would soon learn to define religion in the broadest of terms. You might refer to it as any emotional or reverent belief concerning the meaning of life. To characterize a group of people as being religious solely on the basis of their outward or public expression does injustice to the host of less demonstrative but equally devout individuals. If a person claims to have a religion and he or she receives comfort from it in times of crisis, I will accept it as valid.

The eighteenth-century German playwright and poet Johann von Schiller suggested in his poem "Hope, Faith and Love" three more things of the spirit worthy of inclusion in my list. He wrote in part:

> There are three lessons I would write,
> Three words as with a burning pen,
> In tracings of eternal light,
> Upon the hearts of men.
>
> Thus grave these lessons on thy soul,
> Hope, faith, and love; and thou shalt find
> Strength when life's surges rudest roll,
> Light when thou else wert blind!

After such eloquent words, how could I leave out hope, faith, and love? What's more, your parents would not want me to. They would echo von Schiller's words with equal passion.

Memories, kindness, the mysteries of birth and death, grief, bereavement, and finally guilt round out a list of ten things of the spirit I want to discuss.

I have never seen a patient grow old or face death who did not embrace in some fashion or other some form of religion. This submission can manifest itself by strict adherence to long-standing denominational dogma and ritual, by abstract metaphysical contemplation of

215

the meaning of life itself, and by everything in between. I suppose there are some people who are so agnostic that they would deny that a religious thought had ever crossed their minds, but as age and death creep up on them, their numbers seem to decrease dramatically.

Those who throughout their lives have conscientiously practiced their religion will increase that devotion as the years race by. They will struggle to perform their religious routines in spite of illness, inclement weather, or conflicts in schedule. They will talk about their religion and what it means to them more than ever before. They will seek out every possible religious experience and will pray with deep reverence. They will guide their remaining days by their religious principles, and from them they will gain tremendous comfort and peace.

Those who define religion more as a way of life—that is, by being unselfish, loving, and honest—may begin to express their beliefs in a more organized fashion as their time begins to run out. They may once again seek out the church of their forefathers and take a more active role in religious life. They too find comfort and peace in their revitalized faith.

Many continue to worship quietly. They reveal to the outside world little about how they feel or what they believe. Do not be misled by these less demonstrative individuals into believing that their religion is of any less importance to them than yours is to you. Cultural backgrounds dramatically influence the way different people show their religious feelings. By now, you should know your parents' heritage and customs well enough to recognize and accept their religious practices. Respect them. Encourage them.

Most of us have seen pain and suffering turn the most irreligious person into a believer overnight. If sincere in this conversion, the person adds to his or her life a powerful supportive force. However, most of us have also seen nonpractitioners who, when faced with a situation they could not control, implore the grace of God as if He and they were on the best of speaking terms. If perchance they recover, they forsake their new-found faith as if by reflex. One sees this erratic behavior most often in busy emergency rooms. Yet I cannot disparage their efforts even if it gives only momentary comfort. Someday their fleeting faith may become more permanent.

The religion that plays such a major role in your parents' later years may conflict with your own current beliefs. Indeed, religious canons do change from generation to generation, if not in fundamentals at least in methods of expression. Remember, your parents may be one generation behind you in their thinking. If there have been arguments in your family over religion in your earlier years, you may be hard pressed to avoid them now that such matters have taken on new emphasis. Your parents may not only try to get their own religious house in order but may seize upon the opportunity to try to get yours in order as well.

Try to understand and respect their present feelings. Just as you would not deny them a miraculous antibiotic, do not deny them the miracle of religion. A person with a deep abiding faith has a force on his or her side that no medicine can match. It can raise a person's tolerance for pain and suffering better than a narcotic. As the individual undergoes anesthesia, it can give him or her the confidence that he or she is in the hands of someone more powerful than mortal man. It can help your parent accept his or her destiny with grace and dignity. Faith is a powerful and tranquilizing treasure.

Your parents' growing dependence on religion is in a certain way a growing independence away from you. It is a transference of support from you to something more powerful. Accept it. Use it. Promote it. Be willing to embrace whatever they find comforting, even if it means that you might have to put on a momentary false front in their presence. Pray with them, talk with them, commune with them. Take them to their church, synagogue, or meeting house if they need transportation. Read to them from whatever printed word gives them comfort. Let them enjoy their religion and never, never belittle their preoccupation with things of the spirit.

If your parents are still healthy and active, these religious manifestations may not have yet taken on their eventual significance—but they will in due time. Recognize them when they do appear and accept them as a normal and proper response to the process of aging.

However, I would hesitatingly like to add a word of caution. Rapid changes in religious practices or pathological overemphasis on religion may indicate the onset of mental illness. Unfortunately, the line between normal religious expression and abnormal religious fanaticism is very thin. If you are unsure, do not hesitate to seek professional advice. Bizarre actions, response to voices, irresponsible transfer of funds, or harmful changes in daily activities such as eating, sleeping, dress or speech, all in the name of religion, suggest a need for the individual to undergo professional evaluation. It is tragic to realize that such a helpful and comforting resource as religion can be distorted by a troubled mind. But since it can happen, it is best to be forewarned.

If and when your parents are institutionalized, their need for religious support may increase, even become paramount. Most hospitals and nursing homes have a mechanism by which they can provide such care. If geographically convenient, it is best if this can be supplied by their own pastor, priest, rabbi, or other religious leader. If that is not possible, the institution will arrange for such support through some local clergyman of your parent's own denomination or by a trained chaplain. These latter individuals, much as in the military, handle the religious needs of all denominations in an equally loving manner. Although ordained in some specific religion, these graduates of special chaplaincy programs know and understand the requirements of all religions; they know when to intrude and when to back off; they know that family support is essential for peace of mind; they know that things confidential should not pass their lips; and they know that many little worldly deeds in times of crisis take on a spiritual significance. They do not try to convert or condemn, but attend to the things of the spirit in a most enlightened manner and at a most essential time.

Learn to know whoever is in charge of your mother's or father's spiritual care. Help that individual comfort your parent by supplying him or her with whatever relevant information is at your disposal. This may help avoid the many little acts of omission or commission that might otherwise prove embarrassing. A skilled hospital chaplain is a valuable resource. Use him.

Unfortunately, there may be a misfit here or there as in any walk of life. Usually inept chaplains are weeded out very early, but if you find your parent is upset, misinformed about his or her condition, or is in any way made uncomfortable by such an individual, do not hesitate to complain. Usually a friendly request to the nurse in charge will be sufficient. If the problem is severe or persists, contact your parent's attending physician who can terminate the relationship by written order. In such cases, the remedy is not to terminate all spiritual support, but rather to find an acceptable substitute.

Von Schiller's hope and faith need only minimal elaboration. Who is there among us who would not agree? But we also might ask, "Who among us understands the implications these hold for our own parents, particularly as they get up in years?" Obviously, each of these spiritual attributes varies with the individual's own emotional, cultural, and personal experiences. Yet, each can take on a special meaning, as von Schiller says, in times of crisis.

I have seen hope in patients when there should have been only despair, faith when there should have been only resignation. Where this power comes from, I cannot say, but I know it exists. It cannot be bottled. It cannot be held in your hand. It cannot be prescribed from a pharmacy, but every physician knows it exists. Often ordinary physicians or surgeons appear to be miracle workers when the credit should go to the patient and his or her undying faith, not to the skill of the doctor. Although these individual strengths and powers cannot forever nullify life's inevitable release, their presence fills the hearts of the health professionals assigned to the care of those lucky souls having them. Things just seem to go better in such patients. We like that. Hope and faith are very infectious and spread to everyone with whom these patients come in contact. Do not underestimate this force. Instead, bring hope to your parents, bolster their faith. Your long experience with your parents should have taught you the words, the expressions, the actions that breed and nourish hope and faith in them. Aging parents need every ounce of support you can muster in nurturing these two special things of the spirit.

Love, von Schiller's last attribute, is an overused word emblazoned on banners and souvenirs, embraced by cults, and espoused in prurient literature, but it still represents life's deepest, purest, and most universal emotion. Your parents showered it upon you from before you were born, and they will crave it till their own hearts are stilled. In fact, their need is perhaps greatest when they become old and face that one experience for which there can be no practice. If you talk to the elderly, particularly the sick elderly, and ask them what they most want from their children, it is love. Can I define what they mean? No. Can I offer a formula or the ingredients that make up love? No, but that hasn't stopped me from talking about it. Since 1960 I have quoted in articles and on the public platform Leo Tolstoi's reference to love in his essay "The Fundamental Law of Human Life." He wrote:

> It all lies in the fact that men think there are circumstances when one may deal with human beings without love, and there are no such circumstances. One may deal with things without love, one may cut down trees, make bricks, hammer iron without love; but you cannot deal with men without it, just as one cannot deal with bees without being careful. If you deal carelessly with bees, you will injure them and will yourself be injured. And so with men.

I can only add, "and so with your parents."

In the autumn of life there is little left to anticipate but much to remember. Under certain conditions, time treats us well. It seems to mellow our memories and brightens them far beyond reality. All life's little irritants, minor tragedies, lost possessions, and broken promises are forgotten as the happy moments of life are elevated to new heights. Occasionally, exaggeration overpowers facts and transforms a somewhat unpleasant experience into a catastrophe, but usually with the passage of time real tragedies are brought back to mind only briefly, accepted as fact and returned to storage. It is the joyful moments that grow with time.

Therefore, your role is primarily one of helping your aging parents enjoy their many pleasant memories, the good old days, your childhood, family celebrations. You will tire of hearing them over and over again, but listen with tenderness and tolerance. If you are interested in either genealogy or family history, twist your parents' predilection for reminiscing into a constructive recording of history. This can be accomplished in a number of ways. The simplest is having your parents write it down or tell it to you so that you can write it down. If the material is important enough, the interviewing may be done by a third person as long as that person does not hamper the free flow of information. An older grandchild makes a wonderful reporter. Your parents will love to talk, and your child will love to listen. Getting the kid to write it down is another matter! The use of a tape recorder might seem to be the most logical solution, but many older persons do not take too well to such mechanical gadgets. I tried that once, and it didn't work. Consequently, I lost information that should have been saved. It is amazing how much valuable family or even regional or national history is lost because nobody takes the time and trouble to record it. The realization of its importance comes too late. My wife and I regret that some of the family history our parents knew so well is now lost forever. If your parents are artisans in one form or another, you certainly will save the things they cross-stitched, painted, carved, or crafted. But what if they are musicians? Have you recorded some of their music? Now is the chance before they lose their skill or dexterity. Remember, memories, like light itself, spread in all directions. Let your parents enjoy their memories, but let some of them bounce off for you to treasure as well.

Do you remember when you were a child how anxiously you looked forward to birthday presents, to gifts you received on various holidays, even to something from the tooth fairy? At your present age these gratuities probably seem unimportant to you, but remember, they have become important again to your aging parents. Could this also be, in part, what they mean by second childhood? You will never know how much a flower, an inexpensive trinket, a photograph, a postcard—anything from you to them—will mean to your parents until you give it.

Although my wife and I faithfully visited her widowed mother at the retirement home in which she lived, my wife still sent her a steady stream of "care packages" as her mother called them. My wife, who would remember every holiday from Valentine's Day to New Year's, would never send expensive gifts, but merely a few favorite candies, a paperback book or two, or some new trinket or grocery item her mother may not have seen. Each was wrapped with pretty paper and ribbon befitting the occasion. Her mother loved those presents. She would set them out on her coffee table still unopened to show her friends before they all shared in the mysterious contents. She did confess that on occasions when she didn't want to spoil the wrappings for a few days she would carefully slit the bottom of those she thought contained books, slip them out, and replace them with ones she had already read.

Yes, such remembrances, such tokens of kindness, mean a lot to our elders. They are a tangible sign of love, of thought, and of appreciation for who they are. Isolation is dispelled and warmth fills its place. Yet not all kindness should be in the form of gifts. Much should come from the deeds you do, the errands you run, the shopping trips you make, the times you drive them to church or to the doctor, your having them over for dinner, your taking them to see a play or a parade, or taking them on a picnic in the woods. Don't you alone "stop and smell the flowers" as the song goes. Let your parents enjoy a whiff along the way as well!

Some of the happiest memories your parents will ever have will concern births: yours, those of your siblings if you had any, and those of their grandchildren, great-grandchildren, and other close relatives. In contrast, their saddest memories will be the deaths of their own parents, of any of their children or grandchildren, and, of course, the death of their own spouse if that misfortune has already occurred. Most adults who have lost one or both of their parents could not have realized before that tragedy how frequently memories of their mother or father would flash back in their minds. With that revelation, you can imagine how sorrowfully your parents look back at the loss of relatives and friends. The pain passes; the memories persist.

A part of old age seems to be reading obituary notices and attending funerals. I am constantly surprised at how little outward emotion many of the elderly show at the loss of their friends. They must hear that immutable ticking of their own internal clock, yet they accept reality, at least outwardly, as if it did not personally affect them. I do not wish to say that they are unmoved or calloused by such events. Quite to the contrary, they just accept them differently than you or I might. If you accompany your parents to the funeral of one of their close friends, be prepared to witness this disciplined reaction. Do not initiate conversation unless you are sure how it will be accepted. Rather, play it by ear. Follow your parents' lead, and do not let your own feelings or emotions color the conversation. Unless you suspect some ulterior motive in their remarks, go along with them, support them. At that moment your concern should be for your mother and father, nothing else.

If there ever is a time when things of the spirit become dominant, it is at the time of your own parent's death. As I mentioned in Chapter 13, "Homes Away from Home," it will be an event that will wring not only every human emotion from you, but from your parent as well. If you have never witnessed the death of someone close to you, your mind will be full of questions. You may even feel panic or frustration. Death does not follow a simple, well-organized, or uniform plan. Rather, each death is an individual experience influenced by a myriad of variables: the disease or trauma itself, its speed, the person's resistance, their will to live, the professional care they receive, the effectiveness of family support, the location, and even the time of day.

Before death occurs, your parent may pass through five loosely defined stages. The first is *denial*. Once your parent has recovered from the shock of learning that death might be imminent, he or she will deny that such a catastrophe could occur. "It must be a mistake," he or she will argue. "Look at me. I haven't lost any weight. It can't be." As the truth sinks in, *anger* will be substituted for fear and anxiety. Your parent will thrash out. He or she will ask, "What have I done to deserve this?" Your parent may become provocative, even abusive. This stage too will pass, and he or she will begin to *bargain*. Your parent will plead with the physician and will try every quack scheme. He or she will go to the ends of the earth for a cure or do anything that might promise hope. When this fails, your parent falls into a deep *depression*. Hope is gone. Nothing is left. Yet from someplace within his or her soul, your parent eventually finds *acceptance*. He or she admits the truth, acknowledges the outcome, and mellows. Your parent looks at his or her life and family differently, and an inner peace—which is hard to believe unless you have seen it—settles over the patient. Obviously the progression through these five stages is not necessarily or-

derly, uniform, or absolute. There are wide variations, but if you observe one or more of these typical reactions, you will know that others
have traveled the same road before. Try to accept each stage for what
it is. Work through each one and help your parent pass on to that final
stage in which he or she can find inner peace.

Often the specter of death dawdles along at a slow, emotionally
draining pace, making management more difficult. It is true that there
are those who peacefully close their eyes and fall into eternal sleep,
but if one's final days are not handled properly, they can be wracked
with pain, nausea, difficulty in breathing, or tormented by other bodily problems. Should this happen to your mother or father, you will
probably ask, as others have asked before you, "Where can he or she
be best cared for during these difficult final days, weeks, or months?"
Although 70 to 80 percent of all deaths occur within hospitals,
nursing homes, or hospices, they can take place at home with equal
dignity. In fact, this time-honored practice appears to be returning.
However, the location is not as important as the environment in
which it takes place. That environment involves you and the rest of
your immediate family as well as the professionals assigned to your parent's care. It involves what you say and do, and what you do not say
and do not do. It involves the love, the caring, the physical and emotional support, the security, and all the devotion and human kindness
one can share with another at such a critical time. Above all, it involves the wishes of the patient. Such requests are absolute, and the
courts of the land will uphold such desires provided they are not from a
patently deranged mind. Because of the recent advances in medical
technology, there are now quasi-legal documents called "living wills"
or "death with dignity wills" that people in good health prepare ex-
pressing the manner in which they would prefer to be treated should
they ever be unable to make those decisions themselves. These statements generally ask that their dying not be unduly prolonged and that
medication be given to reduce pain, even if it may hasten death. Although not legally binding, the responsible relatives generally acqui-
esce. For these and many other reasons, the location of the deathbed
matters little. It is the atmosphere, the environment in which the final days are spent, that makes the difference.

Unfortunately, there will come a day when the end nears. Of
course, you will feel sorry for your mother or father—that is only natural. But remember, most elderly, as the rest of us, would like to live
forever, provided we could be active and could enjoy reasonably good
health. On the other hand, we would not want to live forever if we

were in pain and thoroughly miserable. Consequently, many elderly patients face death willingly. They have accepted its inevitability and are anxious to be relieved of their suffering. They feel that they have lived their long years well and do not want to spoil it by an unhappy and uncomfortable end. Their primary fear, other than the possibility of physical discomfort, is the thought of being abandoned at the end. They want you and their families with them; they want to talk about old times, good times. They may or may not want to wrap up certain loose ends such as who gets what, where the will is located, what the final arrangements should be. Ideally, of course, these matters should have been discussed long ago. On the other hand, some may say, "It's all up to you. Do what you think best. It won't affect me anyway. Just hold my hand." Family problems may be aired one last time in a final attempt to resolve them. Compassion flows to and from each other as at no other time. Use it; receive it; be cleansed and challenged by it; and give it back in return.

Unfortunately, you will probably not be at your best during these last days. You will not know what to say or how to say it, and you will tend to clam up or to babble about things inconsequential. But don't. Keep talking about what your parent wants to talk about. It may be about his or her fear of pain, of isolation, or of the unknown. Your mother might worry about what will happen to some member of the family who is having money, job, or family problems. She will not easily give up her concern for the family, and you wouldn't expect her to.

Many at this stage worry about their deteriorating appearance, about unfulfilled dreams or ambitions, or what will become of some treasured possession. They will try to hang on to the control of their lives as long as possible. Let them keep their own schedule, do their own thing. If they want some ice cream in the middle of the night, give it to them. If they want to select what nightclothes they are going to wear, let them. They've lost control of the big things in their lives, so don't deny them control of the little things. Kindness at this stage of one's life can unfortunately be a two-edged sword. Not enough is cruel; too much can steal away one's independence. Try to find the right balance, but above all, enter into some meaningful dialogue. You will not have that chance much longer.

Many middle-aged sons and daughters as well as other relatives and friends of a dying individual may suffer what is called "anticipatory grief." Such feelings are understandable, even natural, but they have to be handled. They cannot be permitted to become incapacitating. If they begin to adversely influence your behavior to the point of affecting others including your dying parent, seek help. Usually a member of the clergy, a physician, a social worker, a nurse, or a valued friend can offer the support you need. They have seen it before and can understand the pressures. Occasionally, more professional support is required to return such a person to constructive behavior.

I have known a few cases where thoughtless and selfish relatives, anticipating the death, have become concerned about their inheritances and have acted like a bunch of ragpickers. Most parents with any property will have made plans for its disposal in their will. The deathbed is no time or place for such a discussion unless your parent brings it up. Then it will usually concern things of sentimental value, not the bulk of the estate. How cruel some selfish relatives can be!

In a few rather pathetic cases, prolonged coma, overpowering trauma, or severe mental confusion will steal away this golden opportunity to share together these precious last few moments. But be careful. Medically, we cannot accurately tell when all sensations cease. In spite of apparent unresponsiveness, there may still be hearing, feeling of a hand holding theirs, or of a kiss or caress. Therefore, do not hold back signs of affection. Rather, temper your speech and actions so that the wrong message will not get through.

Rarely you and your family might be faced with the situation where your parent's life is being maintained only by artificial life support systems. If, by examination, he or she has been found to have suffered brain death and there is no chance for survival without the machines, the decision to terminate the life support involves the family, the physician, and, at times, the courts. There is no easy answer. It can only be made by bringing together all the medical, moral, legal, and ethical forces consistent with such a grave decision.

At some time and place the end will come. It will be a personal experience for which you will have no adequate preparation, so you will have to handle it in your own way. Hopefully it will be in an emotionally mature manner. If either your mother or father survives the death of his or her partner, direct your full attention to him or to her. He or she will need it, not for an hour, not for a day, but for a painfully long time. For both you and your remaining parent the passage of time will eventually ease the pain, reduce the depression, and permit life to return to a new equilibrium—not as before, but in a new phase where life can go on in peace.

Whenever there is a death, someone has to make arrangements for the disposition of the body. If you are the next of kin, this task will fall to you. If there is a surviving spouse or if you have siblings, you may still be asked to share in that responsibility. Although this might technically be considered your last obligation in the care of your aging parent, it is a field outside of my expertise and, therefore, outside of the purpose of this book. However, you need not travel that road alone. If you already have a funeral home you know and trust, fine. If not, consult your clergyman for guidance. Although state and local consumer groups in some areas offer helpful information, you cannot get it on a moment's notice. Therefore, you will have to do some quiet preplanning. But whatever you do, seek competent advice. Do not stumble through alone and unprepared. Help is there for the asking.

My greatest concern at this time is to help you minimize the guilt that may surface during your parent's terminal illness and funeral. Unfortunately, guilt can overshadow sadness at this emotional time depending on one's earlier conduct or on one's false perception of how he thinks he may have acted or should have acted. None of us can do much about the past—that's water over the dam. But the funeral is not the place to try to cleanse one's soul of guilt. I have never heard of a case where a person prior to his or her death asked that money be wasted on an unnecessarily elaborate funeral just to make a guilty child feel better. In many cases your parent will have set the boundaries, so follow them. Also follow your own good common sense. This is not the time for excesses, show, or self-therapeutics. Provide dignity, but do not turn your parent's last rites into something completely inappropriate just to prove to yourself and to others that you were not what you really were. That will only create a new and continuing guilt, the feeling that you tried to buy your way out of the first one. It would be better to forget the spilt milk, if indeed it was spilt. Resolve not to let it happen again with your remaining parent, thereby avoiding guilt the next time around. But for this time, forget it. Grow from the experience, don't get sick over it.

Fortunately, most middle-aged sons and daughters will have no guilt. If that is because they demonstrated their love and devotion to the fullest when it was most needed, bless them. They earned their peace. I just hope it wasn't because they were so insensitive to their abandonment of their parents that they did not recognize their failure.

Summary

To help you evaluate what should be done at this sad time, let me offer three simple but guiding statements to keep in mind:

For the Family. Terminal illness and death are family matters and should not be left to strangers. The alternatives of care should be adequately presented and explained by the patient's attending physician, but the patient with the support from his or her own immediate family, no one else, should choose which to accept and which to reject. Care at this time includes many facets, physical, financial, emotional, spiritual, and everything else relevant to the patient and his or her environment except, of course, for those decisions where medical judgment is necessary.

In those cases where the patient is being cared for in the home by members of the family, respite care should be provided. This is a system of temporary placement of the patient in some appropriate health care facility on an inpatient or day care basis to permit the caregivers at home some necessary rest.

For the Patient. There should be a competent, continuous, and caring system of medical care provided by both the attending physician and, if and when necessary, by the personnel and facilities of a hospital, nursing home, hospice or home nursing service. If the patient is at home, these professionals should offer backup assistance for any crisis that might occur. This combination of talent and facilities should control the patient's pain and other distressing symptoms to the fullest extent possible. The same team should be available to answer questions, offer advice, and help make those arrangements concerning the patient that the family might be either unfamiliar with or unable to handle alone.

For the Survivors. There should be both counseling and emotional support for the family members particularly for those closely involved with the care and maintenance of the patient. Support for anticipatory grief and bereavement should be available to the extent required or desired by individual family members. Professional help should be available for those who in their bereavement also suffer from guilt.

Finally, the best lesson this bewildering experience can offer is to serve as a role model for your own old age. Adopt what was beautiful, and cast aside what was not. Accept with grace what is inevitable and, as your parents did, draw strength from the things of the spirit.

CHAPTER 17

Three Ways
to Cope

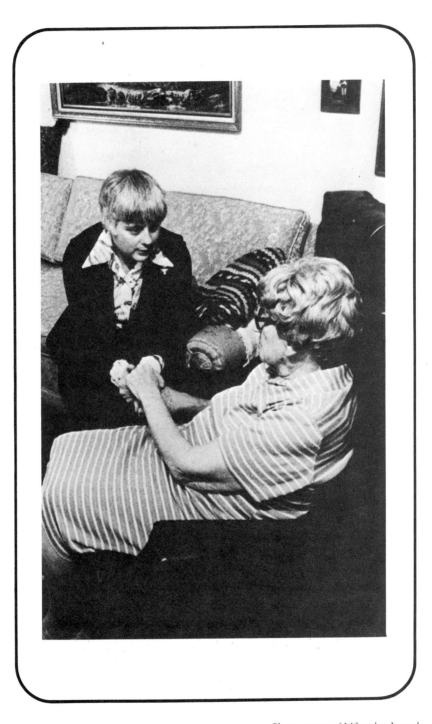

Photo courtesy of Milwaukee Journal

"*I* can't stand it any longer. God only knows, I can't." No, these are not the distraught words of an aging parent suffering from a terminal illness. Rather, they are the woeful cries of a harried, middle-aged caregiver who has been physically and emotionally drained by taking care of a sick and aging parent day in and day out. These few words give a clear sign that this person can no longer cope, that his or her coping mechanisms have broken down.

This occurs most frequently and most devastatingly when one or both aging parents are ill or incapacitated and are being totally cared for within the home by one member of the family, usually a daughter or daughter-in-law. The stress of coping tapers off as one moves step by step away from this highly personalized responsibility toward the opposite extreme where both parents are in reasonably good health, are voluntarily institutionalized at their own expense in some retirement facility that is able to provide high-quality comprehensive care on a continuing basis and that is located some distance from the home of their children. In both of these extremes and in every situation in between, there are ups and downs, good days and bad. However, there will never be a day of zero stress, no day that does not require some element of coping.

As people differ in their physical and mental capabilities, so do they in their ability to handle stress. Some let it roll off, others let it boil inside. Therefore, you must first know your own tolerance to stress and your own ability to keep things under control. Coping does not start when the stress of caring for your aging parents first appears. Unless you have your own life together and have established a comfortable self-image and a healthy lifestyle, the problems of dealing with your parents will be overpowering. You will not bring to it a solution, but rather you will be part of the problem. So straighten out your own life before you try to assume responsibility for the care of your aging parents.

The coping process is doubly difficult if you and your spouse are on different tracks. If what bothers one doesn't bother the other, and vice versa, another whole area of stress and conflict can loom. Work out these differences, minimize them as much as possible, and then understand, tolerate, and decompress the differences that remain.

Do not underestimate the damaging effects of stress. Your body reacts to the difficult task of caring for your aging parents as if it were trying to escape from danger. Your pulse quickens, your blood pressure

231

goes up, the vessels in your heart dilate as those in your abdomen contract, your blood-clotting mechanism springs into action, your immune system shuts down, your stomach increases its production of
acid, your eyes widen for better vision, and your muscles tense as if
getting ready for action. These physiological responses were created
eons ago to protect you from dragons. If your body can't tell the difference between your aging parent and a dragon, you will be under constant stress. Illness will follow as surely as night follows day, and you,
the caregiver, will become sicker than the one you are caring for.

Therefore, stress must be handled. However, it does not take
very profound analysis to realize that there are only three ways to
handle stress and to cope. They are:

1. To reduce those factors that cause stress
2. To improve your ability to cope with whatever stress remains
3. To share your stress with some outside agency willing and able
   to assist you in handling your specific stressful problems

To put it more succinctly, lower your stress and raise your coping
ability.

Reducing the Stress Factors

Let us first look at some of the ways you might be able to reduce the
factors and problems that lead to stress. Some will involve your parent
or parents, some will involve the environment, and some will involve
you and other caregivers.

Placing distance between yourself and your parents is not something that I would unconditionally recommend, but it is an effective
way of reducing some of the problems that lead to stress. Of course, it
might also create additional stress within your parents and enough
guilt within yourself to cancel out any possible gain. If the separation
is the result of your parents voluntarily entering a full-service retirement community, fine. If they are to be taken care of by someone else,
relative or not, also fine. Both moves should reduce your stress.
Therefore, count such a venture as a blessing but hope that the distance will not be so great as to prevent frequent visits.

It will be much more stressful for your parents if you and your
family have to move away to some distant city because of the
relocation of the breadwinner, and they can't or won't accompany

you. Your move to a foreign country at this time of their lives might cause a reaction close to panic. Hopefully, you should be able to accept emotionally the necessity for such moves, and although it might increase your sorrow, it should not cause any guilt. However, travel, phone calls, and letter writing will be an added stressful chore for both of you and expensive to boot.

But what about those other situations when your parents live either in your own home or within close walking distance, and you are destined to become the major caregiver? How can you control that kind of stress? Your first thought should be to reduce the stress that might be environmentally induced. Try to get your parents' ecosystem in harmony. There are many things one can do within the environment that will either reduce the irritants which cause stress or prevent the minor or even major accidents which certainly will increase it. Some are easy to accomplish, others more complicated. Some require physical alterations, others expensive purchases. But for the sake of completeness I shall mention them all, and in cafeteria style you may pick those that most appeal to your tastes and pocketbook.

The ideal physical environment for an elderly individual or couple living in your home, even if they are without major incapacities, is a separate room or suite. It should have a safe and convenient exit to the outside by being located either on the first floor, or if you live in a multistory dwelling, the building should have an elevator. Of course, the choice will ultimately depend on the architectural layout of your home or apartment. If you and your parents can avoid going up and down stairs, you will be fortunate indeed. Although the room should be convenient during the day, it should not be isolated at night. A simple bell, buzzer, or call system of some type will help bridge what might otherwise be an awkward arrangement. An intercom system is helpful, particularly if one of your parents is bedridden part or all of the day. It will help avoid those double trips to get what the person wanted in the first place. It need not be fancy. Those sold in hobby or electronic stores would do fine.

The room itself should be large enough to accommodate both a sleeping and sitting area. It should be furnished with pieces that your parents have chosen for both comfort and sentimental value. Hopefully, the furniture will be without sharp corners and will not tip over or slide easily if inadvertently leaned against. The bed should be without casters, offer easy access, and have a firm mattress. If both your father and mother occupy the same room, twin beds offer less disturbance to the other partner and, in case of illness, permit easier care. If one or both have special medical problems, there might be the need for a hospital bed, one which can be cranked into various positions. This maneuverability can be very helpful not only for your parent's comfort but particularly for your own. As nurses learned many years ago, stooping over a low bed is the bane of a caregiver's existence. It is almost a guarantee for low back pain. If your parent is mentally confused, and many elderly are, particularly at night, use protective rails or other barriers at the sides of the bed. However, they should not be of a kind that would force the patient to climb over them. That would only increase the height of the fall. Rather they should serve both as a barrier as well as a support when the occupant does wish to get out of bed. These are often called *half-rails*. If your parent is totally bedridden, full siderails should be up whenever he or she is not being attended to.

A rocking chair in the room not only brings nostalgia but surreptitiously promotes movement and circulation. Avoid vinyl fabrics or plastic covers on chairs as they can get uncomfortably hot or cold. Scatter rugs are taboo for obvious reasons, as are shaggy loop carpets or waxed floors which might cause tripping or slipping. Incidentally, there should be one or more comfortable—and easy to get in and out of—chairs in every room to which your parents might routinely go such as the living room, family room and, if big enough, even the kitchen. This will make your whole home more welcome to your parents and reduce any feelings of alienation or isolation.

If your parents live in a two-story house and one of them is wheelchair-bound much of the day but can navigate stairs either on his or her own or with help, a wheelchair for upstairs and another for downstairs will be tremendously helpful.

Most people pay little attention to doorknobs, but they can become barriers to the weak or arthritic. If they are hard to turn or are small and slippery, replace them with larger, more textured knobs or glue on covers of heavy fabric.

Color is important to our moods, regardless of age. Therefore, use warm, light colors to brighten the spirit and aid in your parents' depth perception. Avoid the depressing blues, violets, or grays. Contrasting colors or textured materials may be used to set off structural features that promote orientation. Plenty of natural daylight as well as a pleasant vista is desirable. If there is glare, it should be reduced by sheer curtains or venetian blinds as many elderly are sensitive to extremes of light. A dimmer switch on the bedroom ceiling light or on a lamp is often convenient as is a night-light placed low enough to illuminate a path to the bathroom.

The heating and cooling of the room is important because the elderly's temperature-control mechanism is not as adaptable as the rest of the family's. If a thermostat is available to the household members, you will find that the elderly turn it up and the young turn it down— always, of course, when the other is not looking. It would be better to discuss the realities of this situation and agree to make the adjustments with clothing, not with the thermostat. The elderly can use shawls and lap robes while the younger members can dress to their preference. Since the elderly often get up during the night, the nighttime temperature setback should not be as drastic as it might be in a more normal household desiring to conserve energy. Cooling is much the same as heating, but in reverse. Chilling should be avoided. However, an individual confined to a bed or chair is more comfortable and his or her skin is less irritated if there is no appreciable sweating. Be tolerant of your parents' tendency to complain about the temperature. They do feel discomfort when you might not. It's not obstinacy, it's physiology.

Storage of your parents' personal belongings can be a problem if not conveniently placed within their reach. Poorly placed articles can be one more irritant for them and one more interruption for you. Consequently, put their things at mid-level, easy for them to see, arrange, and reach. Garments should be placed one per hook. If the closet has a light, make sure the switch cord is long enough. If they use the kitchen, avoid cabinets above the stove as they are particularly dangerous for the elderly who may have poor vision, impaired balance, and flowing sleeves. Cabinet handles can be raised or lowered to better accommodate the individual with reduced range of motion or who is confined to a wheelchair.

For a partially or totally handicapped individual, the bedside table becomes his or her medicine cabinet, beauty shop, recreational area, office, snack bar, hobby shop, convenience store, emergency warehouse, and light and power company. Therefore, make it big enough and convenient enough to serve these diverse functions. Since accidents will happen regardless of layout, add some facial tissues and maybe even a roll of paper towels.

You can add a number of other items to your parents' room that will help them keep in touch with reality, the time of day, the day of the week, and outside people and events. A telephone can provide both security and enjoyment, particularly to the handicapped, by helping them keep in contact with friends and relatives and maintaining some control over their own lives. Depending on how long you might think your parent's room will be used, you might first consider getting a long extension cord rather than having a fixed installation put in by the telephone company. Many hardware stores and all the new telephone stores sell adapters that will permit you to rig up telephone service temporarily to a sick room with or without a new instrument. But be careful that no one trips over the wire. Of course, if your home or apartment is relatively new, there should be phone outlets in every room—which will make moving the phone very easy. However, you may still want a long cord so that your parent will not have to move or stand up to make or answer a call. If one of your parents is visually handicapped, you might consider either a phone or an adapter with large numbers. As a word of caution about telephones, let me remind you that unless your parents are of sound mind, they can do as much mischief on the phone as your young children. You don't want them dialing Australia.

Since television is such a part of life these days, rig up a set in your parents' room. If they are bedridden, place it in a comfortable viewing position. A remote control device will save a lot of running around on your part and a lot of aggravation on theirs. Unfortunately, they are expensive gadgets and are not available for all sets. Television is a good mind distractor for the elderly and the bedridden, but, as I have repeated so often, it does not stimulate much mental or physical activity. Remember, movement of the joints, stimulation of the circulation, jogging of the memory, and the maintenance of other necessary bodily functions are not helped by inactivity. Therefore, make sure your parents do not spend their entire day watching soap operas and game shows. Keep them moving, busy, and alert.

Your parents' room certainly should not be bare or sterile. Rather, it should be warm and homelike. In addition to decorative items, it should contain a few other essentials. A clock with a large face and bold numerals is useful, but make sure it does not have an irritatingly loud tick that could disturb the light sleeper. A calendar should be hung from the wall in full view of the bed, preferably one that shows only one day and date at a time in big letters. If one or both parents are mobile, it should become their chore to tear off the outdated page at the beginning of each day. It will force them to face the reality of day and date. An appointment book or calendar kept at the bedside or, at least, within their room will help them keep track of future events.

As we learned earlier, it is important to stress good grooming. Consequently, place at least one mirror in the room. A full-length mirror is especially helpful as it might save some embarrassments of dress that can frequently occur in elderly people with poor agility, dimmed vision, or faulty memory. If it can be placed so that it gives the occupant either a view of the entrance hall and the oncoming visitors or an expanded view of the room or outdoors, so much the better.

Flowers or plants not only add a feeling of life to a room, but their care will give purpose and responsibility to your parents as they work with them. Even if you, the caregiver, end up tending the plants, it will bring you into the room for something other than the care of your parent or parents. It will open up an opportunity to talk about something other than their complaints and needs.

Depending on the interests of your parents, the time they spend confined to their room, their state of health and many other variables, you can do other things to liven up the room. Add mobiles; music systems; reading materials; all sorts of crafts and hobbies; pictures of grandchildren, other family members, and friends. Although the room may appear cluttered, except for dusting, who cares?

It goes without saying that there should be a bathroom conveniently close to your parents' bedroom. This necessary facility deserves special attention because it is a frequent source of tragic accidents. Since most existing bathrooms cannot easily be redesigned for the aged or handicapped, every effort should be made to maximize the efficiency and safety of the one you do have. First consider the floor. Bathroom carpeting is preferable to small mats or wet slippery floors. Many toilets are low and difficult for an elderly or handicapped person to sit down on and to get back up from. Your drugstore can sell you a relatively inexpensive raised toilet seat attachment that slips on and off a regular toilet bowl and places the seat at a comfortable position. There are also portable grab rails that encircle the toilet on both sides and permit the individual to pull him- or herself up. Unfortunately, when you use such devices, the original paper holder may no longer be in a convenient position, but it is easy to arrange some alternate placement.

The bathtub and shower require special caution. Grab bars are helpful regardless of the age and agility of the bather. Although a nonskid surface on the bottom of the tub is helpful, do not use any material that would be uncomfortable or irritating to sit on.

As I said in an earlier chapter, scalds are always a danger. They can be prevented only by keeping the household hot water supply at a temperature no greater than 120° Fahrenheit and by exerting extreme caution when bathing. Such accidents happen to the elderly because they are not quick or agile enough to either turn the water off or to escape the dangerous environment. Believe me, a scald is a tragic sight. Actually, caution more than structural changes, will prevent bathroom accidents, so raise the caution flag and wave it continuously.

How far should you go to make your parents' environment stress- and accident-free? That depends on many factors. Few homes can be modified to one's complete satisfaction. Compromises have to be made. Obviously, you should first work on those items that will have the most beneficial effect at the least possible cost. However, these items may be quite different from person to person and from one house to another. In general, your parents will prefer arrangements similar to those with which they have been familiar. They are less likely to de- mand amenities with which they are not accustomed.

Privacy, however, will be a particularly sensitive issue regardless of one's past. You and your family will lose some of yours, and your parents will lose some of theirs, causing stress on both sides. Even the most favorable physical arrangements will not completely erase all dif- ficulties. Because space will have to be shared, there will be a ten- dency on your part and even on theirs to alter previous social patterns. You will be reluctant to invite your friends over, particularly if you sense there could be some conflict over age, dress, speech, ethnic background, politics, occupation, or a host of other reasons. At first that might seem to be the best move in order to avoid conflict, but it is a poor solution. Don't modify your own lifestyle and particularly that of your children. If you do, you and they will feel cheated, and that will cause more stress. If your parents are physically able to join you when you entertain, allow them that privilege. If they entertain, they should reciprocate. Each side will soon learn if it wants to participate in the other's activities and for how long. Try putting your mother in charge of refreshments. It will give her something constructive to do. Let her do the same for the noisy teenagers. They will learn respect for the elderly, and your mother will experience a life review of her own youth.

Solitude, time away from your task of caregiver, is necessary to maintain your own sanity. Build free time into your schedule, not just for a weekly night out or when shopping, but daily. Midmorning is a good time for the caregiver. Late evening is another. A man and wife certainly should not have to retreat to their bedroom at night in order to have some free time to talk, read, write, sew, watch TV, or just plain loaf. Your children also should not be denied their normal activities. Since your parents need the same opportunity to be alone, try to schedule these periods of solitude mutually.

Sharing a bathroom, if necessary, will be one of the most difficult parts of having your parents in your home. There is no magic formula for removing bottlenecks, but rules must be laid down and a schedule must be set if nature doesn't make one for you. Extra shelves and towel racks should be installed and assigned to each member of the family. Certain functions, such as grooming, can be moved to the bedrooms or even to a small console table and mirror placed ouside the bathroom door. If the man of the house, any maturing juniors, or, even grandpa would use an electic razor, there might be less need to use the bathroom. Use any trick you can think of to keep traffic moving.

There is no question about it. Improving the environment should reduce much of the stress that occurs when you and your parents share your home. But there is more than the environment to worry about. There is your ability to cope.

Improving Your Ability to Cope

Whenever there is a change in the family structure, that change is felt throughout the entire family. Each member must adjust to the new situation, and that takes time. Each member must learn to cope with the stresses that change creates, and that too takes time. Eventually, the transition is complete, the disruption is over, and everyone accepts his or her new role and responsibility.

Unfortunately, in many cases this peace and tranquility never fully come about. If one or both of your parents are difficult to handle for any reason, there is little chance that complete harmony will ever be restored. Some conflict and stress are almost inevitable. Since their care will undoubtedly interfere with your own time and space, it's only natural that you may well begin to feel cheated and put upon, even if you were a part of the decision to have your parents move in. But your only solution, your only chance for survival, is to learn how to cope with the environment in which you have been thrust. Don't fight it. Accept the fact that your parents are now living with you. Since you cannot do much about it now, relax and enjoy it. Recognize that there will be problems. Do not set unrealistic goals. Do the best you can. Your performance will not be perfect, but don't feel guilty about what is not done. You can only do so much.

Considering the stress, it is not surprising that we see some middle-aged sons and daughters trying to cope by overeating, utilizing alcohol, or drugs, or by resorting to parent abuse or other nefarious and ineffective methods. Obviously, these methods don't work; in fact, they only compound the difficulty. That is not coping—it is copping-out. Tears are no better. They are a good momentary release but not a good method of coping.

True coping is a two-pronged process. To be successful, you must have the ability to control yourself as well as the ability to control those around you. In coping with the aged, you must first understand the psychodynamics of aging. You must know what old age is and what to expect from it. Over the years gerontologists have cataloged the significant signs or characteristics associated with old age. They include slowness of thinking, rigidity, mild impairment of recent memory, reduction in enthusiasm, tendency to depression, narcissism, looking backwards, increase in cautiousness, change in sleep patterns, tendency for daytime naps, and less attention to sexuality and more to one's bowels and other bodily functions. As you think about them, I am sure you could subdivide each trait into smaller identifiable parts or even add a few new ones of your own, but as they stand, they should give you a pretty good picture of what your parents will be like when they get older. Obviously, your parents may not show all these characteristics at once, but rather their appearance may stretch out over many long years. Aging varies from individual to individual—which you may have already noticed—and the older the person, the more likely these traits will appear. Therefore, you may not have yet experienced many of the things that require coping. The one thing that is surprising to all of us is the number of senior citizens who are exceptions to the rule. Some remain clear of wit, enthusiastic, mobile, and productive well past their peers. Don't try to comprehend it. If it happens in your parents, just accept it and be grateful for it.

Whenever you are dealing with one of your aging parents, never get into a win–lose situation. You can't win and you shouldn't lose, so avoid any answer that makes either you or your parent a clear winner. Every problem must be thrashed out, negotiated, compromised, or whatever you want to call it so that when it is all over, both sides will agree with the decision. Then both will know what to expect from the other.

Let us review some of the characteristics that you are likely to experience and that in all probability will be sufficiently disturbing to require some form of coping. One of your early irritations might be your parents' slowness in thinking and their inability to reach a decision with the same speed your own relatively young mind would take. To document this trait, I can imagine a hundred questions you and your family might ask your parents: "Which one do you want, Mother?" "When do you want me to help you with your hair?" "What TV program do you want to watch, Grandma?" "Dad, I'm ready. I thought you wanted to go with me." Your ears will be tuned to a quick response in each of these cases, but you won't get it. All you will get is an irritating pause. For you, time's a'wasting. You want to get going. You have better things to do than stand around in limbo. But limbo it will be—not for long, in fact, not half as long as it will seem—but nevertheless you may have to wait. Perhaps you have been thinking about your question for sometime. You are geared up. In contrast, your parent may be hit cold by the question. If their indecision presents no problem for you, you have no need for coping. But if you shift your weight from one foot to the other, begin to tap your fingers or repeat the question a bit louder than the time before, you are showing stress. You can no more hurry up their answer than you can make a traffic light change by yelling at it. So don't. Wait. The light will change, and your parent will reply as soon as all the circuits get in the right position. But how can you avoid the wait? Prepare your parents for the question a few minutes before you need an answer. Try saying, "Mom, in a few minutes we will have to decide when you want me to help you with your hair." Of course, you couldn't get things ready at that moment if you tried. You will still be busy finishing up something else, but by the time you are ready, your mother will also be ready, and you will reach the crossroads together. That's coping. You worked out your problem without stress. You learned the lesson of the duck hunter. He knows he won't be able to hit the duck if he aimed at it, so he has to shoot in front of it so that his shot and the duck reach the same place at the same time. No big deal. You just have to understand your parents like a hunter understands his ducks.

Cartoonists and playwrights love to emphasize the rigidity of old folks. People relate to it; it's real; it makes them laugh. But for you faced with rigidity day in, day out, you will do anything but laugh. Your parents probably have dozens of little rituals, mannerisms, or opinions that will drive you crazy but which you couldn't change with a sledgehammer. Those good souls who were compulsive in their youth and middle-age will probably get more so in their later years. If their actions are not destructive, don't try to change them. Interference with their little peccadilloes will only increase their anxiety and stress, and, in turn, yours. They may misinterpret your innocent attempt at correcting one of their irritating mannerisms as a deep criticism of their total behavior. As a defense, they may withdraw from the very contacts they need to stay active. If you say "stop" to the elderly, they probably will. Unfortunately, they are likely to stop everything else remotely connected to an action. As a result, a small piece of their world will have been cut away.

This is not to say that some habits can't and shouldn't be changed. Careless use of smoking materials is a good example. Many men and women spend their earlier lives with a cigarette (or cigar) dangling from their lips with no serious risk of fire. It may be a risk to their lungs and heart, but not to fire. As they grow older and less alert and tend to take catnaps, the danger of fire increases. When I was younger, I do not recall seeing burn holes in my father's ties, suits, or in the upholstered furniture, yet in his upper years each was pockmarked with tiny burn holes. Such behavior should be changed. You should not have to spend the rest of that person's life frightened about what might happen. Remember, I said not to get into a win–lose situation. In this case it would be easy for you to win and for your parent to lose. Rather, *both* sides must agree on a course of action. Your parent's smoking problem must be brought up and thrashed out. A few rules may have to be laid down such as "No smoking in bed" or "No smoking unless somebody is in the room." Although I hesitate to control the lives of older people or to take away any of their freedoms or pleasures, there are times when some limits must be set. Often the individuals with these disturbing or dangerous habits will be the first to agree to change once the problem is called to their attention. Some experience minor accidents about which you may never hear a word, but which cause them to reform of their own accord. This often happens with careless smokers, with accident-prone drivers, and with thoughtless jaywalkers. Tactful suggestions laced with lighthearted humor can often improve this kind of behavior, resulting in less stress on your part. But don't try to change their political or social thinking. You cannot. You may discuss such subjects but don't criticize, don't talk down, and don't try to win. Someday you may think that way yourself.

Impairment of recent memory can exasperate anyone who does not realize that it is one of the quirks of old age. You may blow your top when your parents can't remember where they put their glasses or when they agreed to be back for lunch yet can spend a full morning following you around the house telling you in detail what you did when you were a baby. This discrepancy occurs because an aging brain treats recent and long-term memory differently. This can irritate you to the point of screaming, "I told you a million times, Mother, that you have a doctor's appointment this afternoon. You'll have to pay more attention. We can't go on this way." Your stress is showing. Others might try to cope with such a problem by letting the whole business roll off like so much water from a duck's back. Why worry, they say, you can't do anything about it. Well, that's not quite true. The brain, although not a muscle, needs exercise. The electrical pathways work better if they are used. Therefore, take time to help your mother recall when and where she was told about the doctor's appointment. As your parents sit resting, get them in the habit of re-membering what they did that day and what is scheduled for tomor-row. The more remembering they do, the better they will get at it, and the less stress each of you will suffer.

It is often said that the young anticipate and the old reminisce. It's true. And it's easy to blame reminiscing on the fact that the elderly haven't much to look forward to, but it is more than that. They have a need to talk about the past, to live their lives again through stories, photographs, and family history. As I mentioned in Chapter 7, "Lifestyles," we call that "life review." It resolves internal conflicts and validates their very existence. Therefore, don't walk away and don't close your ears. Listen. Appear interested. Ask questions. Force their life review. They may even finish sooner and with more content-ment if they know that you have paid attention. However, if the person has had a hard, unhappy, and traumatic life, stick to those ex-periences that were pleasant or in which the individual made some contribution to society or to someone else. Be complimentary; empha-size the positive. If their reminiscence comes at an awkward time, and often it will, don't just close your ears. Rather, suggest, for example, that they organize their photos or letters and then schedule a time when you can go over them together. You used that trick with your children when you redirected their attention to some attractive alternative, and the same thing works with the elderly. But do not forget your promise to talk together.

Narcissism, defined as an excessive admiration of oneself, is a common reaction in those elderly whose egos have been shattered by those around them. Most people, the elderly included, generally ap-prove of themselves, and they also expect some recognition from those around them. If this is denied, they may start to brag, to cover up, and to exhibit grandiosity, or they may begin to withdraw. If this happens, erase the need for this type of behavior. Shower them with love and with praise. Permit them their happy life review. If you do, they will be easier to live with, less demanding, and much more predictable.

If you poll a group of middle-aged sons and daughters caring for aging parents who exhibit many of the characteristics of old age that I listed earlier, you would find that one of the most difficult and stressful traits for the caregivers to handle is the alteration of sleep patterns. Their rest periods never seem to jibe with those of other members of the family. The old folks take their naps just when the kids come home from school or when you have supper on the table. They go to bed early and then wake up before dawn and prowl around the house waking up everybody within earshot. They wander at all hours of the night as they get up to go to the bathroom. It wouldn't be so bad if no harm could come from all this, but it can. They can wander outside in all sorts of weather; they can get lost; they can fall and trip in the dark; and they can get into every kind of difficulty imaginable. Consequently, every adult in the house has one ear open all night listening for the happy wanderer to start his or her journey. I know of one woman who for six months slept on a cot placed across the bedroom door so that if her aging husband got up, he could not get out without her knowing it. Think what this does to the sleep of the caregiver and of the stress it must engender. If you count up the hours of sleep most old people get in a twenty-four-hour period, you would likely find that, including naps, it comes to seven or eight hours. No loss of sleep there. The loss is all one-sided.

Under such circumstances the temptation is to use sedative drugs in the hope of giving your sleep-disturbed parent a good night's rest. Many nursing homes follow such a routine, but I cannot recommend it for general use. As I said earlier, sedatives produce problems of dependency, leave undesirable aftereffects, and foster mental confusion. A better way is to practice the sleep techniques I outlined in Chapter 11. If there are disturbing noises either inside or outside the house, play soft, relaxing music.

Don't try to cope by taking sedatives yourself. Use the same techniques that promote good sleep patterns in your parents. To these you can add deep breathing, more vigorous exercise, laughter, and any other activity that you find clears your cluttered mind.

Of course, the best way to cope is to experience nothing that requires coping. People being what they are, the best way to reduce your own stress is to reduce stress in your parents. As in physics, if there is no action, there is no reaction. So let me tick off a few suggestions.

First of all, cleanse your mind of all the myths about aging. If you don't, you will either blurt them out unconsciously or will act as if they were true, setting the stage for friction between you and your parents. Remember, just because your parents are old, they are not necessarily sick or useless, senile, or have lost their sex drive. Just because they are old, they will not necessarily end up in a nursing home. Most elderly, at least until they are old-olds, are essentially normal people. Treat them as such. There may come a time when their internal clocks run down, but don't hurry it. Light up their lives as much as you can for as long as you can.

Keep your parents in touch with reality. Talk current events. Use newspapers and TV along with the clock and calendar to keep them aware of the time, date, appointments, and daily routines. Sensory deprivation can cause confusion and abnormal behavior. The more the elderly are confined to small spaces such as to their bedrooms, the greater the sensory deprivation can become. Keep their horizons as wide as possible in all facets of their lives. Don't let them hibernate.

Make your parents feel useful by giving them responsibility, particularly the kind they were used to—such as cooking, sewing, cleaning, keeping financial records, house repairs, or feeding the pets. Let them participate in making those decisions that involve themselves. Don't let them fall into the trap of acting fragile, incompetent, dependent, and don't patronize them. Treat them as the adults they are by avoiding baby talk and allowing them to do the jobs they find difficult to do, such as buttoning, cutting meat, and picking up small things. The more you do, the less they will be able to do for themselves, and soon you will find yourself doing everything and having a difficult time coping. Now, this does not mean you should be cruel. You can tell the difference. Help when necessary, of course, but don't pamper because pampering steals their independence.

Don't hide facts. Old people have faced facts before, and they can do it again. Most of us are poor poker players, unable to hide the truth. If we try, it will be written all over our faces, and our parents will catch us lying, only heightening their anxiety. Since senior citizens are nosy characters, particularly if they feel information is being withheld, give them the truth and they will more likely be truthful with you in return.

Express affection by touching. Hold their hands, kiss their cheeks, pat their shoulders, hug them. A light touch on the inside of the arm is a particularly reassuring gesture reserved for those who are intimate. The elderly need and respond to these types of tactile stimulation. For the elderly, much of sexuality is expressed by touching. Don't mock it. Understand the place of touching in their lives and encourage it.

Do not impose your standards on your parents or let them impose theirs on you. They are bound to be different, so show respect for theirs but expect consideration of yours in return. If there are problems, talk them out together and convince them that most differences are not rooted in right or wrong but are merely reflections of a generation gap.

Keep communications open but make it two-way. Don't make it appear as if you are letting what they are saying go in one ear and out the other. Listen, and don't interrupt or make judgments. Maintain eye contact. Show interest. Respond to their questions. If you are preoccupied at the time your parents want to talk, schedule a time when it is more convenient.

In those situations where your parents live some distance from you and where visits are infrequent, it is particularly important to keep in contact through every possible method at your disposal. A feeling of isolation grows as contacts diminish, and as we saw in an earlier chapter, isolation is a form of parental abuse.

Try not to get yourself in a position where you can be manipulated. Many parents will try such techniques, often quite unconsciously. Some will resort to tears when they do not get what they want, but if you give in to their crying because of some false sense of guilt, you are being manipulated. These individuals will keep on using tears as a method of forcing you to do their bidding. The problem, therefore, is to be able to differentiate between tears of pain and depression and those of manipulation. Act aggressively on the tears that well up because of real problems, but be firm on yielding to tears designed to gain unreasonable demands.

Thoughts of suicide are common in the elderly, particularly in those who are deeply depressed because of some seemingly irreparable loss or disappointment, or because of a painful terminal illness. Unfortunately, suicide follows no completely predictable pattern. Many elderly quietly consider suicide but take no action. Others talk about it but still take no action. Others talk about it and eventually try it with various degrees of success, and still others never talk about it yet do it. Suicide threats are particularly hard to interpret and harder to respond to. Even professionals have difficulty in evaluating the words and signals of suicide. However, if a parent has repeatedly threatened suicide to gain selfish and inappropriate ends, and you give in, you are being manipulated. It may be difficult, but under such circumstances you will have to confront your parent by saying something like, "I understand, and I don't blame you for feeling that way. But I love you too much to believe that suicide is the best solution." If the threat was meant to manipulate, it will not be repeated. If suicide does occur, chances are your words had little to do with the decision. Fortunately, many such attempts by the elderly are unsuccessful, and the underlying causes are sufficiently relieved to eliminate the need for such morbid thoughts. But regardless of the outcome, do not feel guilty. For some, it is their last act of self-determination.

Much of coping is trial and error, but the biggest part is learning that you are not a super-human being, that you have your limits, and that you can do only so much. You can never meet all the needs of all the people all the time, and if you try, you will burn out. Coping is designed to prevent that burnout by finding acceptable ways to handle stress. Others have learned to cope—so can you.

Share Problems with Outside Agencies

You may have noticed that many books on social issues have long appendices giving the names, addresses, and telephone numbers of helping agencies listed state by state. There is no way such a listing could be made for the many subjects we have covered. In fact, it would be a waste of paper because, with the current economic and political climate, the size, location, and functions of many such agencies are being changed. But, you are not alone. Many agencies are willing and able to help you and your aging parents in a myriad of wonderful ways. Furthermore, if you make contact with one agency and they cannot help you, they will refer you to one that probably can.

A good place to start is with your parents' doctor. Unfortunately, many physicians are not as informed about such agencies as they should be. Since this is not their forte, do not hesitate to pursue the matter on your own. Many hospitals have social service departments that can be of tremendous help in steering you through the maze of agencies. Most of them will do this regardless of whether your parent was recently hospitalized or not. Your church may also be an excellent referral source because they probably have answered the same question many times before. There are senior citizen centers in most communities operating either under the auspices of the American Association of Retired Persons or independently. They not only offer healthy diversion to the elderly, but they are a continuing source of information about needed services. The telephone book is the ultimate referral source. It lists the names of all helping agencies, often under multiple headings. Generally, the name of most agencies is specific enough to identify its area of expertise. In many communities the telephone directory has an entry for an Office on Aging, listed either alphabetically or under local governmental services. Some communities have an information center that you may call to find out which agency serves your need. If financial aid is required, your first call should be to the local office of Social Security, the second to the county welfare department. If your parents are not eligible for governmental help, the staff will usually be able to refer you to some local agency that has just the program you need.

The message here, of course, is to seek help, not to suffer alone. Even if there is no specific problem, you may find an agency or program that would enrich your parents' lives. This would not only help reduce stress in them but ultimately in you as well. Not all of these helpful programs serve only the elderly. Many are concerned with such general areas as nutrition, safety, recreation, transportation, specific diseases, rehabilitation, alcohol abuse, housing, and many, many more. Check them out. You may be pleasantly surprised.

The problem we see most often is that people fail to use the agencies that could be of service to them. They do this, in part, because of their ignorance of the existence of such agencies but more often because of their mistaken belief that such services are available only to the indigent and that using such services is somehow demeaning. That is just not true. Most agencies have a broader mission. They want you; in fact, they need you to stay in business.

So remember, share your problems with the appropriate agencies. It is one of the smartest techniques you can use to help cope with the heavy responsibility of caring for your parents whether they are ill or just up in years.

The rewards for taking good care of your aging parents are many, yet such rewards do not come without sacrifice. However, coping can reduce that sacrifice without blunting the rewards. Therefore, learn to cope. You will be glad you did.

CHAPTER 18

The Final
Challenge

Photo by *Virginia Kraucunas*

*T*hroughout this book I have tried to offer as many practical and specific suggestions as possible considering the breadth of the subject. I have tried to bring you facts about the elderly, how they think, how their bodies work, and what their needs might be. I have tried to widen your vision and promote your understanding. I have suggested that you drop the false myths about old age and accept the elderly as people deserving special attention because of their wealth of experience and because of their lifelong contribution to their families and to others.

I have warned about the value as well as the dangers of the drugs they take. I have emphasized the need for good nutrition and for a healthy lifestyle. I have described their various living arrangements, both at home and away. I have stressed the importance of safety, the need for physical and mental stimulation, and the place religion plays in their lives.

I have listed the many medical problems that particularly befall the old-olds, those above seventy-five years, and have offered suggestions for handling those illnesses and disabilities. I have warned that mental and emotional problems stalk many of the elderly and that their care is often made more difficult because of such turmoil. Yet I have advised that competent medical and psychiatric care can often modify such behavior, giving hope to the depressed, clarity to the confused, and contentment to the agitated.

I have also suggested that both you and your aging parents should put life in its proper perspective. Expect neither paradise nor utopia. Life is not like that, not at any age. Problems abound, and they fall unevenly and unjustly. Perfection is seldom if ever reached. Compromises must be found and accepted. No one is exempt—everyone must learn to cope, to find ways to take care of both themselves and their aging parents.

I have begged you to distinguish between doing your best and reaching for the impossible. I have challenged you to do the first but refrain from the latter. Unless you accept this difference, you will enjoy no inner peace and may even lose your normal emotional equilibrium. What's more, you will remain unnecessarily guilty, not appropriately fulfilled.

Yet in spite of this, I have rather blatantly urged you to make a deeper commitment to the care of your aging parents. You may have questioned why I have repeated the obvious, assuming that devotion to one's parents is the norm in our society, the way most people act. Indeed, for many it is, but unfortunately for others it is not.

One can readily measure the lack of caring by the amount of guilt which tears at the heartstrings of so many otherwise kind and thoughtful people who upon the death of a parent ask themselves "Why didn't I visit Mom more often? She must have needed me, but now she is gone, and it's too late"; "Why did I fight so with Dad? I still think I was right, but why did I make such a fuss, so much that it tore us apart? Now I can't even apologize to him"; or "With Sis being so close to Mom and me so far away, I wonder if she died thinking I didn't care."

Unfortunately, few of those who abandon their aging parents are spared from asking themselves these cruel questions. Guilt burns deep and often into their saddened hearts.

Meanwhile your own children have been witnessing everything that has been going on and have been getting signals as to how they should act when they grow up in the not too distant future. Provide them with the right example. Remember, much of the neglect we see is due to a lack of knowledge and understanding, not intent.

I do not want to appear insensitive, but may I suggest in the most gentle manner that you ask yourself how you and your parents are getting along? Are you comfortable or do you have twinges of guilt? If you do, now is the time to do something about it. Now is the time to analyze your performance. Certainly, I have no difficulty in assuming that you conform to the highest standards of conduct in most facets of your daily life. Most people do, yet I would be a bit surprised if every middle-aged son or daughter felt totally happy with the way he or she has acted toward his or her parents.

There are many extenuating circumstances in life that keep us from doing what we would like to do. Long distances tragically separate many children from their parents. Travel is expensive and so are telephone calls. Even the cost of mail makes it difficult for some. Time must be spent with one's growing children. Work must be done around the house. Every holiday and vacation cannot be spent at grandma's, and your spouse certainly deserves every bit of time and attention you can afford. That's a lot of pressure and a lot of commitment, I recognize that. I also recognize that I cannot set your priorities for you; I cannot commit your funds, nor can I allocate your free time. I certainly cannot foretell what the needs of your own parents might be. As we have learned, they can vary immensely. But I can say with some degree of certainty that if you do not spend enough time and effort in loving and caring for your parents, they will suffer an unnecessary sense of isolation, and you will suffer an unnecessary sense of guilt.

Now is the time for middle-aged sons and daughters to make a commitment to care for their aging parents in whatever manner seems appropriate to their parents' individual needs. For some, where the needs are small and the distances short, the effort may be rather insignificant. For others, it may be close to overwhelming. But once your aged parents are gone, there will be no tomorrow, no chance to make a renewed commitment, no opportunity to do for them what they did for you when you were a child.

And now for one final lesson in preventive medicine. If perchance your parents' lives were either made more burdensome or cut short because of some unhealthy lifestyle, they may have unwittingly given you their final piece of parental advice: to protect your own future by following the simple rules of good health and by avoiding those accidents and diseases we know are preventable. It is a proven fact, based on an analysis of the leading causes of death in the United States, that unhealthy behavior and unhealthy lifestyles account for some 50 percent of the mortality in this country. What a waste! Therefore, may I challenge you to observe every possible helpful habit while you still have the time in order that someday you may become a healthy and happy aging parent.

Index